Shanghai Maths One Lesson One Exercise

(Grade 5, First Semester)

Series Editor: Prof FAN Lianghuo
Consultant: Dr Lionel PEREIRA-MENDOZA

华东师范大学出版社

图书在版编目(CIP)数据

一课一练. 五年级数学. 第一学期 = Shanghai Maths One Lesson One Exercise (Grade 5, First Semester): 英文/范良火主编. —上海:华东师范大学出版社,2017
ISBN 978-7-5675-6607-1

Ⅰ.①一… Ⅱ.①范… Ⅲ.①小学数学课-习题集-英文 Ⅳ.①G624.505

中国版本图书馆CIP数据核字(2017)第176305号

Shanghai Maths
One Lesson, One Exercise
(Grade 5, First Semester)

主　　编　范良火
总 策 划　倪　明
组稿编辑　徐慧平
特约审读　王善平
装帧设计　高　山

出版发行　华东师范大学出版社
社　　址　上海市中山北路3663号　邮编200062
网　　址　www.ecnupress.com.cn
电　　话　021-60821666　行政传真 021-62572105
客服电话　021-62865537　门市(邮购)电话 021-62869887
地　　址　上海市中山北路3663号华东师范大学校内先锋路口
网　　店　http://hdsdcbs.tmall.com

印 刷 者　常熟高专印刷有限公司
开　　本　890×1240　16开
印　　张　13
版　　次　2017年8月第1版
印　　次　2019年6月第2次
书　　号　ISBN 978-7-5675-6607-1/G·10450
定　　价　48.00元

出 版 人　王　焰

Preface to the English Language Edition

This English language edition of *One Lesson One Exercise* series is based on the latest Chinese edition of the *Yi Ke Yi Lian* series, a multiple award-winning bestseller, published by East China Normal University Press. Since it first appeared in the early 1990s, the Chinese edition of the *Yi Ke Yi Lian* series has been regularly revised and used by millions of students in primary and secondary schools all over Shanghai and beyond. The awards it has won include, for example, an official listing by an authoritative organization of China's book industry in 2009 as one of the China's "300 Most Influential Books in the 30 Years since Reform and Opening Up" (1978 - 2008), and in 2015, the series was awarded the title of "Shanghai Famous Trademark" by the Shanghai Administration for Industry and Commerce for the third time, the only book (series) awarded the honour by the Administration.

To keep the originality and authenticity of the Chinese edition, the English language edition is essentially a direct translation of the Chinese edition, so the loss of meaning in translation is kept to a minimum. When it is not possible to have a direct translation, necessary adjustments or changes have been made. For example, in Chinese, a Deng Shi (e. g. $2+3=5$) is different from a Fang Cheng (e. g. $2x-3=7$); however in English, the word "equation" can apply to both a Deng Shi and a Fang Cheng. In this case, the questions in the Chinese edition were slightly changed when possible or deleted otherwise in this English language edition. When appropriate, a footnote has been added to remind the readers of the difference from the original Chinese edition. For readers' convenience, a Chinese-English mathematics glossary is also added in each book of this English language edition.

Recognising the importance of doing adequate practice in the learning of mathematics, we have two main aims in publishing this English language edition. The first is for it to serve as a useful resource for school students, teachers and parents, not only in China but also in other countries, in their learning, teaching and tuition of mathematics using English as a medium. The second is to provide an important window for international readers, in particular mathematics teachers, mathematics education researchers and policy makers, to look through and thereby to understand better the content, pedagogy and assessment of Chinese mathematics teaching and learning in schools, as reflected in this series of learning resources.

It should be noted that the *One Lesson One Exercise* series was originally developed for the use of Shanghai school students to enhance their learning of mathematics, though more and more students outside Shanghai or even China have also used this series because of its reputation. Following the Shanghai school system, the series consists of 17 student practice books: one book for each semester for all the five primary grades (Grades 1 to 5) and the first three secondary grades (Grades 6 to 8), and one for the final secondary grade (Grade 9).

Many people have supported the translation and publication of this series, in various ways. I wish to record my special appreciation to Professor Tim ROWLAND and Mrs Judy ROWLAND of the United Kingdom, Dr Lionel PEREIRA-MENDOZA of Canada, and Professor Zalman USISKIN of the United States for the consultation work they generously offered for the series at different grade levels. My sincere gratitude also goes to Ms Ellen CHEN, Dr JIN Haiyue, Dr Jane LI, Dr LU Rugang, Mr NI Ming, Ms XU Huiping, Mr XU Jing and Dr ZHU Yan for their assistance at different stages.

Professor FAN Lianghuo
Series Editor

Chinese-English Mathematics Glossary for Grade 5 (First Semester)

中英文数学词汇对照表(五年级第一学期)

English	中文
base	底，底边
bottom base	下底
calculator	计算器
composite figure	组合图形
decimal	小数
decimal with one decimal place	一位小数
decimal with two decimal places	两位小数
decimal with three decimal places	三位小数
diagonal	对角线
equation	方程，等式
evaluate	求值(动词)
evaluation	求值
height	高
hundredths place	百分位
isosceles trapezium	等腰梯形
letter	字母
mean	平均数
mixed decimal	带小数
mixed operation	混合运算
natural number	自然数
parallel	平行
parallelogram	平行四边形
perpendicular	垂直
perpendicular foot	垂足
pure decimal	纯小数
quadrilateral	四边形
recurring decimal	循环小数
recurring period	循环节
remainder	余数
right-angled trapezium	直角梯形
simplify	化简(动词)
simplification	化简
solve	解(动词)
solution	解
symbol	符号
tenths place	十分位
thousandths place	千分位
top base	上底
trapezia	梯形(复数)
trapezium	梯形
value	值
unit	单位
whole number	整数

Contents

目　录

Chapter 1 Revising and improving

1.1 Using symbols to represent numbers

Basic questions

1. What number does each ○ in the following calculations stand for?

(1) ○ + 2.8 = 17.2
○ =

(2) 10.3 − ○ = 4.7
○ =

(3) ○ × 6 = 120
○ =

(4) 1260 ÷ ○ = 9
○ =

(5) ○ × ○ = 81
○ =

(6) ○ + ○ + ○ = 96
○ =

(7) ○ + 1.3 + 7.7 = 14
○ =

(8) 15.2 − 3.4 − ○ = 1.6
○ =

2. What digit does each △ in the following calculations stand for?

(1)
```
   6 △
+    △
------
   7 2
```
△ =

(2)
```
     △
   2 △
+  △ △
------
   9 8
```
△ =

(3)
```
   5 △
−  △ 8
------
   1 5
```
△ =

(4)
```
   △ △
×    △
------
 1 7 6
```
△ =

(5)
```
     △ 3
×      △
--------
   3 7 8
```
△ =

(6)
```
      △
   ------
 △ ) 2 7
     2 △
   ------
       2
```
△ =

3. Look for patterns.

(1) 1, 5, 9, 13, ∗, 21, 25, 29, □, 37, …

∗ = (   ), □ = (   )

(2) 0.3, 7.7, 0.5, 7.4, 0.7, ○, ☆, 6.8, 1.1, 6.5, …

○=(   ), ☆=(   )

(3) 2, 4, 8, 16, □, 64, 128, ☆, …

□=(   ), ☆=(   )

(4) 0.1, 0.2, 0.3, 0.5, 0.8, △, 2.1, …

△=(   )

4 Fill in the spaces.

(1) Given ☆ × 71 + ☆ < 500, the greatest natural number that the ☆ can be is (   ).

(2) Given 100 > □ × 9 > 30, the natural numbers that the □ can stand for are (   ).

(3) If 125 ÷ ○ = 10……5, then the number that the ○ stands for is (   ).

(4) If 12 + ◇ = 3 × ◇, then the number that the ◇ stands for is (   ).

(5) Given $\frac{1}{2} > \frac{1}{\square} > \frac{1}{10}$, there are (   ) ways to fill in the □ with a natural number.

(6) What numbers do the △ and ○ stand for?

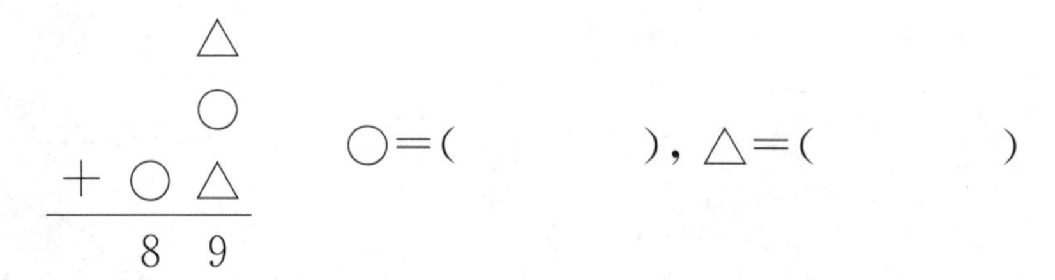

○=(   ), △=(   )

Enhancement and extension

5 Look for patterns and then fill in the ○ with suitable numbers.

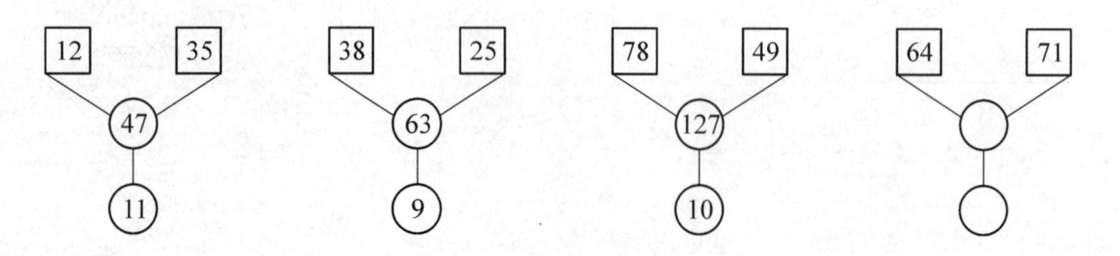

6 Study the pattern that the natural numbers are arranged and then calculate.

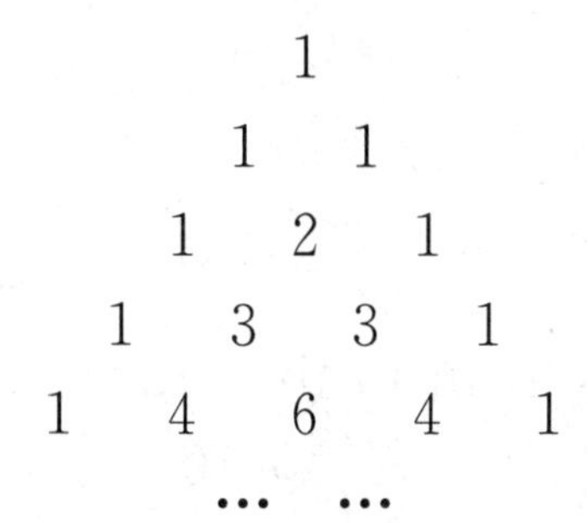

The sum of all the numbers in the eighth row, counting from top to bottom, is (　　　　).

The number in the middle of the eleventh row is (　　　　).

1.2 Decimals (1)

Basic questions

1 Think carefully and then fill in the brackets.

(1) 15.792 consists of ( ) 10, ( ) 1s, ( ) 0.1s, ( ) 0.01s and ( ) 0.001s.

(2) The number that consists of 2 hundreds, 3 tenths and 4 thousandths is ( ).

(3) A decimal whose whole number part is zero is a ( ) decimal. It is ( ) than 1.

(4) $318.79 = 300 + (\quad) + (\quad) + 0.7 + (\quad)$.

2 Simplify the numbers using the property of decimals.

0.0110= 6.0600= 120.000=

3 Rewrite each of the following numbers as a decimal with three decimal places without changing its value.

0.56= 3= 10.2=

4 Fill in the brackets.

(1) $0.07 \xrightarrow{\times 100} (\quad)$ (2) $6.9 \xrightarrow{\div 10} (\quad)$

(3) $0.18 \xrightarrow{\times 1000} (\quad)$ (4) $3.6 \xrightarrow{\div 1000} (\quad)$

(5) $12.5 \xrightarrow{\times (\quad)} 1250$ (6) $60 \xrightarrow{\div (\quad)} 0.006$

(7) $(\quad) \xrightarrow{\times 100} 80$ (8) $(\quad) \xrightarrow{\div 1000} 0.28$

(9) $0.005 \xrightarrow{\times 1000} (\quad) \xrightarrow{\times 100} (\quad)$ (10) $4.7 \xrightarrow{\div 10} (\quad) \xrightarrow{\div 100} (\quad)$

5 Unit conversion.

(1) 1.35 kg = ________ g　　(2) 780 kg = ________ t

(3) 15.4 L = ________ mL　　(4) 30 000 mL = ________ L

(5) 0.08 m = ________ cm　　(6) 8080 m = ________ km

(7) 4.2 km^2 = ________ m^2　　(8) 0.5 t = ________ g

(9) 10 dm^2 = ________ m^2　　(10) 150 cm^2 = ________ m^2

6 Application problem.

Our country's Shenzhou V spacecraft is 9.2 metres long and weighs 7790 kilograms, while the Shenzhou VI spacecraft is 9.2 metres long and weighs 8 tons. Of the two spacecrafts, which one is heavier?

Enhancement and extension

7 Fill in the ○ with operation symbols and the □ or (　　) with numbers.

(1) 4.7 $\xrightarrow{\div 100}$ (　　) $\xrightarrow{\bigcirc\square}$ 0.47

(2) (　　) $\xrightarrow{\times 1000}$ 3.4 $\xrightarrow{\bigcirc\square}$ 0.034

8 Compare and then calculate.

Every 10 g of dried prawn contain 3.93 g protein and 0.2 g calcium, while every 100 g of milk contain 3.3 g protein and 0.12 g calcium.

(1) How much protein does 1 g of dried prawn contain?

(2) How much calcium does 1 kg of dried prawn contain?

(3) How many grams of protein does 10 kg of milk contain?

(4) How much calcium does 1 t of milk contain?

1.3 Decimals (2)

Basic questions

1. Work these out mentally and write down the answers.

$0.2 \times 100 =$ $6.3 \div 10 =$ $1.8 + 8.2 =$

$1 - 0.08 =$ $9.6 + 3.04 =$ $25.2 - 5.2 =$

$3.3 + 7.7 =$ $8.8 - 1.5 - 6.5 =$ $9.8 + 0.3 + 9.7 =$

$1 - 0.25 + 0.75 =$ $7.6 \times 10 \div 100 =$ $8.2 - 3.1 + 0.9 =$

$1.2 + 0.18 - 1.2 + 0.18 =$ $0.36 + 0.9 + 0.64 + 8.1 =$

2. Use the column method to calculate. (Check the answer to the question marked with *)

(1) $98.27 + 2.73 =$ *(2) $2.3 - 0.23 =$

3. First observe the differences between the questions, and then work them out step by step.

(1) $92.8 - 52.6 + 27.4$ (2) $92.8 - (52.6 + 27.4)$

4. Calculate smartly.

(1) $5.78 + 4.5 + 4.22$ (2) $4.82 + 7.9 - 1.82$

(3) $84.67 - (14.67 + 15.3)$ (4) $31.2 + 24.58 - 11.2 + 16.42$

5 Multiple choice questions.

(1) When '0' is added to the end of each number below, the number whose value will change is (　　)

(A) 0.24　　(B) 2　　(C) 2.4　　(D) 24.00

(2) Calculating $8.06 \div 100 \times 10$, the result is (　　).

(A) 0.806　　(B) 8.06　　(C) 80.6　　(D) 806

(3) In 20.01, if the decimal point is first moved three places to the left and then one place to the right, the result is (　　).

(A) 0.020 01　　(B) 0.2001　　(C) 2.001　　(D) 20.01

(4) Put 5600 m, 5 km 60 m, 5.006 km and 5 km 660 m in order from the greatest to the least. The second one is (　　).

(A) 5600 m　　(B) 5 km 60 m　　(C) 5.006 km　　(D) 5 km 660 m

6 Application problems.

(1) A rope was 10 metres long. First 2.8 metres was cut off and then another 4.2 metres was cut off. What is the length of the remaining part of the rope?

(2) Xiao Pang had 580 yuan pocket money. Over a weekend, he went to a stationery store with 60 yuan and spent 42.8 yuan on some items for his studies. How much pocket money did he have left?

Enhancement and extension

7 Given that ⓐ stands for a+a+a, and $\boxed{b}$ stands for $b-0.25$, calculate the following.

(1) (0.95) + $\boxed{0.8}$　　(2) (0.8) − $\boxed{0.95}$

1.4 Decimals (3)

Basic questions

1. First fill in the numbers on the tree diagrams, and then write the steps of your working.

(1)

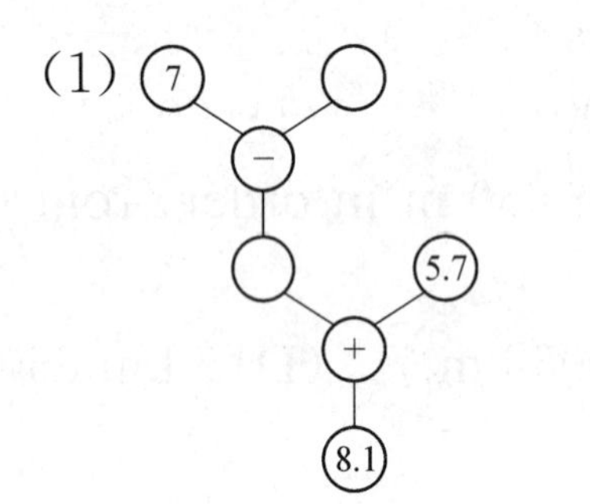

(2)

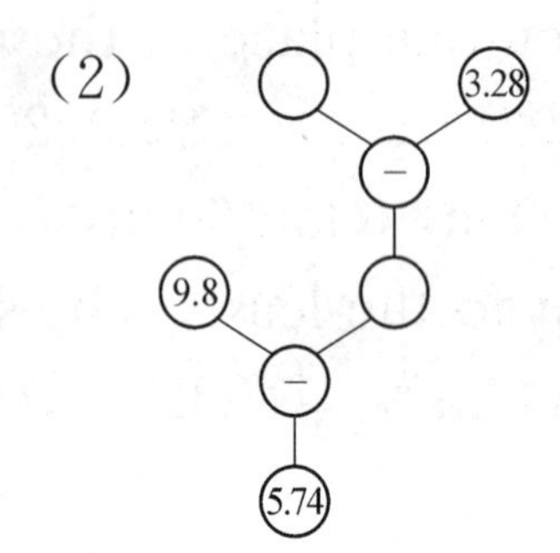

First calculate: ________ First calculate: ________

Then calculate: ________ Then calculate: ________

2. First draw a tree diagram, and then use the method of working backwards to find the answer.

Guess the age: Xiao Pang and his family were celebrating his grandma's 80th birthday. One guest asked Xiao Pang: 'How old are you?' Xiao Pang gave a riddle for the guest to guess: 'Multiplying my age by 6 and then adding 8, it will be my grandma's age. Make a guess, how old am I?'

Tree diagram: Number sentence:

3. Calculate as indicated.

(1) $\square - 5.37 + 1.73 = 9$

First calculate: ________ Then calculate: ________

Mixed number sentence: ____________________

(2) $19.9 - (\square + 5.45) = 10.1$

First calculate: ________ Then calculate: ________

Mixed number sentence: ____________________

4 Use your preferred methods to find out the numbers in $\square$.

(1) $15.25 + \square - 0.75 = 18.65$ (2) $29.6 - (\square - 18.7) = 9.3$

5 Application problems.

(1) River workers were measuring the depth of a small river. They put a 4-metre-long bamboo pole vertically into the water. The part in the mud was 0.58 metres and the part above the water was 1.27 metres. What was the depth of the river?

(2) Xiao Dingding is 0.03 metres taller than Xiao Pang. Xiao Qiao is 0.05 metres shorter than Xiao Pang. Xiao Qiao is 1.42 metres tall. How many metres tall is Xiao Dingding?

(3) A fertilizer plant produced 85.6 tonnes of fertilizer on the first day, 2.56 fewer tonnes than on the second day. On the third day, it produced 6.45 fewer tonnes than on the second day. How many tonnes of fertilizer did it produce on the third day?

Enhancement and extension

6 Xiao Ming had some pocket money at the beginning of September. He first spent 35.8 yuan on items for his studies, and then in a weekend, his grandpa gave him another 120.7 yuan. After that, he spent 67.2 yuan on subscribing to some newspapers and magazines, and now he has 589.4 yuan left. How much pocket money did he have at the beginning of September?

Unit test 1

A. Calculation problems. (50 marks in total)

1 Work these out mentally and write down the answers. (6 marks in total)

$0.4+0.46=$ $\quad$ $0.58+0.42=$ $\quad$ $10\div1000\times100=$

$7.5-0.25=$ $\quad$ $5.3+4.7\times10=$ $\quad$ $5+3.04+0.96=$

2 First write down your working and then write the answers in the $\square$. (6 marks in total)

(1) $48.3-\square+59.6=84.2$ $\quad$ (2) $67.3-(7.68+\square)=24.4$

3 Use the column method to calculate. (Check the answer to the question marked with *) (6 marks in total)

*(1) $35.6+149.4=$ $\quad$ (2) $9.07-1.88=$

4 Work these out step by step. (Calculate smartly if possible.) (24 marks in total)

(1) $3.68+7.56-4.56$ $\quad$ (2) $35.6-1.8+14.4-7.2$

(3) $30.6-(10.6-5.8)+4.2$ $\quad$ (4) $7.85+2.34+1.15+4.66$

(5) $90.8-19.28+10.72$ $\quad$ (6) $0.9+0.99+0.999+0.111$

5 Write the number sentences and then calculate. (8 marks in total)

(1) 14.2 is added to 8.6 and then minus 0.44. What is the result?

(2) The sum of 2.8 and 3.3 is subtracted from the sum of 18.9 and 11.2. What is the difference?

B. Application problems. (30 marks in total)

6 The area of the oceans on the surface of the earth is about 3.61 hundred million square kilometres, which is 2.12 hundred million square kilometres greater than the land area. How many hundred million square kilometres is the total surface area of the earth?

7 A warehouse had 38 tonnes of food to be delivered to a disaster-hit area. In the first delivery, 7.25 tonnes of food were dispatched. The second delivery was 1.2 tonnes less than the first delivery. The third delivery was 1.45 tonnes more than the second delivery. How many tonnes of food were dispatched in the third delivery? How many tonnes of food were still left?

8 In a long-jump competition, Xiao Ya jumped 2.84 metres, which was 0.55 metres further than Xiao Dingding. Xiao Pang jumped 0.17 metres further than Xiao Dingding. How many metres did Xiao Pang jump?

9 An electrical appliance store has a promotion on a special brand of microwaves. The original price was 880 yuan. The price was first reduced by 80.5 yuan, but it was found that the sale did not go well. The price was then further reduced by 102.9 yuan. What is the price of the microwaves now?

10 Two pieces were cut off a steel rod 8.4 metres long. The first piece was 2.8 metres long, which was 1.9 metres shorter than the second piece. How many metres long is the remaining part of the steel rod?

11 A school was organising an autumn outing and Xiao Ming went to a shop near the school to buy food.

Sesame biscuits: 7.55 yuan per pack	Fruit juice: 4.5 yuan per bottle
Cream biscuits: 8.68 yuan per pack	Soda: 3.6 yuan per bottle
Sandwich buns: 2.8 yuan each	Sausages: 9.8 yuan each

(1) He wanted to buy one pack of cream biscuits, one sausage and one bottle of fruit juice. How much would be the total cost?

(2) If he wanted to change to buy one pack of sesame biscuits, one sandwich bun and one bottle of soda, would 15 yuan be enough? If so, how much would be left? Otherwise, how much would he be short?

C. Concept problems. (20 marks in total)

12 Simplify.

30.040=(　　　　　)　　　　3.040 400=(　　　　　)

13 Rewrite these as decimals with two decimal places.

7.8=(　　　　)　　　　4.100=(　　　　)

14 Unit conversion.

2.8 m=(　　　　　)cm　　　　138 mL=(　　　　　) L

14 256 cm^2=(　　　　　)m^2　　　　1.52 km^2=(　　　　　)m^2

4.43 yuan=(   )fen
7.08 tonnes=(   )tonnes (   )kilograms

15 Following the pattern, think carefully. What number does each symbol below stand for?

(1) 1, 2, 4, 7, 11, ○, 22, 29, □, 46, …
○=(   ) □=(   )

(2) 19, 9, 17, 8, 15, 7, △, ◇, 11, 5, …
△=(   ) ◇=(   )

16 Write the numbers that each symbol stands for in the brackets.

(1)

```
      ○ ☆
×     ○ ☆
─────────
    □ □ □
  □ □ □
─────────
  4 □ □ 4
```

○=(   )
☆=(   )

(2) If △.□+□.△ = 15.4, then the least value of △.□=(   ).

(3) If △×△+△÷△ = 50, ○+○−△ = 2011, then △=(   ), ○=(   ).

(4) If (□+□)+(□−□)+(□×□)+(□÷□) = 400, then □=(   ).

(5) There are three numbers *A*, *B* and *C*. Number *A* is 1.2 greater than Number *B* and Number *B* is 2.7 less than Number *C*. If Number *C* is 12.5, then the sum of the three numbers *A*, *B* and *C* is (   ).

(6) Study the pattern that the numbers are arranged. The number in the third place from left to right of the fifteenth row from the top is (   ).

```
        1
      2   3
    4   5   6
  7   8   9   10
11  12  13  14  15
      …   …
```

Chapter 2 Multiplication and division of decimals

2.1 Multiplying decimals by whole numbers (1)

Basic questions

1 A toy windmill costs 5.8 yuan. How much do 8 toy windmills cost?

Xiao Dingding: Let me estimate first.

$8 \times$ ☐ $=$ ☐ yuan. So it must be less than ☐ yuan.

Xiao Pang: I do it by unit converting.

5.8 yuan $=$ ☐ jiao, $8 \times$ ☐ $=$ ☐ (jiao), ☐ jiao $=$ ☐ yuan.

Xiao Qiao: I change it to multiplication of two whole numbers.

$8 \times 5.8 =$ ☐

↓ $\times 10$ ↑ $\div 10$

$8 \times$ ☐ $=$ ☐

That is: 8×5.8

$= 8 \times 58 \div 10$

$=$ ☐ $\div$ ☐

$=$ ☐

2 Calculate.

(1) 8×3.2

$= 8 \times 32 \div 10$

$=$ ☐ $\div$ ☐

$=$ ☐

(2) 0.62×4

$=$ ☐ $\times 4 \div$ ☐

$=$ ☐ $\div$ ☐

$=$ ☐

(3) 9×0.135

$=$ ☐ $\times$ ☐ $\div$ ☐

$=$ ☐ $\div$ ☐

$=$ ☐

3 First estimate and then calculate.

(1) $8 \times 0.9 =$

(2) $9.1 \times 7 =$

(3) $10.7 \times 3 =$ (4) $4.55 \times 9 =$

4 Application problems.

(1) A square flowerbed has a side length of 3.6 metres. If it is fenced on all its sides, how long is the fence in total?

(2) Xiao Ming went to a stationery store to buy pencils. The price of each pencil was 0.75 yuan. How much did it cost to buy 9 pencils?

(3) Xiao Pang exercises every day and runs 8 rounds along a sports field. The length of one round of the sports field is 0.28 kilometres. How many kilometres does he run every day?

Enhancement and extension

5 The ground level of a 10-storey building is 4 metres high, and the rest of each level is 3.8 metres high. What is the height of the building?

2.2 Multiplying decimals by whole numbers (2)

Basic questions

1 Convert decimal multiplication into whole number multiplication and then calculate.

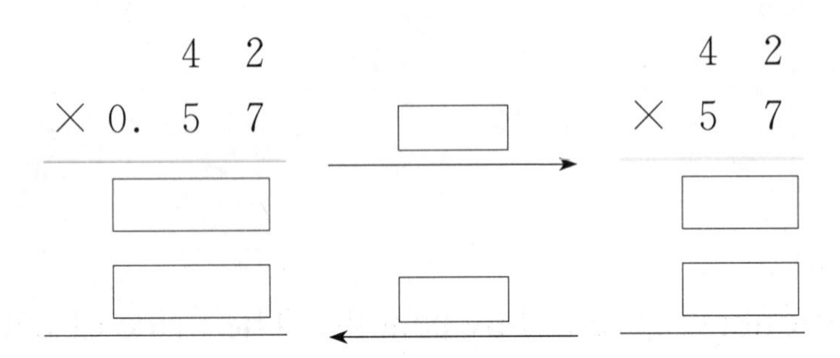

2 First consider whole number multiplication and then calculate.

(1) 29×6

(2) 29×0.06

(3) 47×15

(4) 0.47×15

3 Based on $23 \times 75 = 1725$, work out mentally and write down the products of the following multiplications.

(1) $23 \times 0.75 =$ (　　)

(2) $0.023 \times 75 =$ (　　)

(3) $23 \times 0.075 =$ (　　)

(4) $2.3 \times 75 =$ (　　)

(5) $2.3 \times 750 =$ (　　)

(6) $75 \times 0.23 =$ (　　)

4 Use the column method to calculate.

(1) $7 \times 0.24 =$

(2) $3.85 \times 13 =$

(3) $14.5 \times 18 =$

(4) $25 \times 0.306 =$　　　(5) $10.2 \times 54 =$　　　(6) $23.6 \times 50 =$

5 Are the calculations in the following questions correct? If not, please correct them.

(1)
$$\begin{array}{r} 4.5 \\ \times \quad 8 \\ \hline 3.6\not{0} \end{array}$$

(2)
$$\begin{array}{r} 1.36 \\ \times \quad 250 \\ \hline 680 \\ 272 \\ \hline 34.\not{0}\not{0} \end{array}$$

(3)
$$\begin{array}{r} 3.14 \\ \times \quad 1050 \\ \hline 1570 \\ 314 \\ \hline 471.\not{0}\not{0} \end{array}$$

6 Application problems.

(1) If an object weighs 1 kilogram on the Earth, it will weigh 0.16 kilograms on the Moon. Junjun weighs 39 kilograms on the Earth. If he were on the Moon, how many kilograms would he weigh?

(2) Xiao Ming went to a stationery store with 30 yuan to buy some notebooks. If each notebook costs 4.6 yuan and he wanted to buy 7 notebooks, did he have enough money? Why or why not?

Enhancement and extension

7 A school had an opening ceremony for sports day. The Class 5(1) parade team consisted of 8 rows and the distance between every two adjacent rows is 0.96 metres. How long is the parade team?

2.3 Multiplying two decimal numbers (1)

Basic questions

1 First estimate and then calculate.

A book is 18.6 cm long and 25.4 cm wide. Then its area is about (　　　) cm^2.

Xiao Ya worked this way:

18.6×25.4

$= 186 \times 254 \div \square$

$= 47\ 244 \div \square$

$= \square$

Xiao Qiao worked this way:

```
   1 8.6 ······[  ] decimal place(s)
×  2 5.4 ······[  ] decimal place(s)
---------
     7 4 4
   9 3 0
 3 7 2
---------
 [      ] ······[  ] decimal place(s)
```

2 Fill in the brackets.

(1) $0.83 \times 5.6 = 83 \times 56 \div$ (　　　).

(2) The product of 5.17×3.28 has (　　　) decimal place(s).

(3) Based on $72 \times 25 = 1800$, work out mentally and write down the products of the following multiplications.

$7.2 \times 2.5 =$ (　　)　　　　$0.72 \times 2.5 =$ (　　)

$7.2 \times 0.25 =$ (　　)　　　　$0.72 \times 0.25 =$ (　　)

(4) When one factor is multiplied by 10 and the other factor is multiplied by 100, the product is multiplied by (　　　).

3 Use the column method to calculate.

(1) $8.7 \times 0.9 =$　　　　(2) $0.73 \times 8.5 =$

(3) $1.46 \times 5.4 =$　　　　(4) $28.8 \times 5.5 =$

(5) $20.7 \times 6.9 =$

(6) $8.08 \times 1.05 =$

4 Application problems.

(1) A car travelled from place A to place B at a speed of 78.5 kilometres per hour. It reached place B in 3.8 hours. Find the distance between the two places.

(2) One tonne of plastic waste can produce about 0.8 tonnes of petrol. Then how many tonnes of petrol can a collection of 20.9 tonnes of plastic waste produce?

(3) The speed of a bicycle is 9.5 kilometres/hour, and the speed of a coach is 12.5 times that of the bicycle. How many kilometres does the coach travel per hour?

Enhancement and extension

5 Xiao Ya walks 62.5 metres per minute on average. At this speed, how many kilometres does she walk in 12.8 minutes?

2.4 Multiplying two decimal numbers (2)

Basic questions

1 Calculate the following according to the column method.

Xiao Qiao is drawing a sign board 0.35 m long and 0.28 m wide. The area of the sign board is (   ) m^2.

```
    0. 3 5   ······[   ] decimal place(s)
 × 0. 2 8   ······[   ] decimal place(s)
 ----------
    2 8 0
    7 0
 ----------
  [      ]  ······[   ] decimal place(s)
```

2 Fill in the brackets.

(1) Place a decimal point in the product of each of the following questions.

$0.14 \times 0.3 =$ 42　　　　$0.19 \times 0.26 =$ 494

$0.08 \times 0.12 =$ 96　　　　$0.53 \times 0.017 =$ 901

(2) Based on $36 \times 15 = 540$, write the products of the following questions.

$0.36 \times 0.15 =$ (   )　　　　$3.6 \times 0.015 =$ (   )

$0.036 \times 0.15 =$ (   )　　　　$0.036 \times 0.015 =$ (   )

(3) When a number with two decimal places is multiplied by a number with three decimal places, and the product obtained has only four digits, (   ) zero(s) is/are needed to add to the decimal part when placing a decimal point in the product.

(4) The product of $0.1 \times 0.2 \times 0.3 \times 0.4 \times \cdots \times 0.9$ has (   ) decimal places.

3 Use the column method to calculate.

(1) $1.4 \times 0.07 =$　　　　(2) $0.35 \times 0.08 =$

(3) $1.6 \times 0.024 =$

(4) $0.36 \times 0.11 =$

(5) $0.075 \times 0.28 =$

(6) $2.9 \times 0.026 =$

4 Application problems.

(1) A rectangular board is 0.48 metres long and 0.15 metres wide. Find the area of the board.

(2) 0.16 tonnes of oil can be extracted from 1 tonne of soya beans. According to this, how many tonnes of oil can be extracted from 0.35 tonnes of soya beans?

(3) Xiao Dingding's newly bought home is to be renovated. The area of the lounge is 24.8 m^2. Are 270 square tiles with side length 0.3 m enough to tile the lounge?

Enhancement and extension

5 Number A is $0.\underbrace{0\cdots0}_{24\text{ zeros}}24$, and Number B is $0.\underbrace{0\cdots0}_{125\text{ zeros}}125$. Find the product of Number A multiplied by Number B.

2.5 Multiplying two decimal numbers (3)

Basic questions

1 Put a decimal point in the product of each column multiplication.

(1)
$$\begin{array}{r} 2\ 8 \\ \times\quad 5\ 3 \\ \hline 8\ 4 \\ 1\ 4\ 0\ \ \\ \hline 1\ 4\ 8\ 4 \end{array}$$

Factors printed as 2.8 and 5.3.

(2)
$$\begin{array}{r} 0.\ 3\ 5 \\ \times\quad 4.\ 6\ \ \\ \hline 2\ 1\ 0 \\ 1\ 4\ 0\ \ \\ \hline 1\ 6\ 1\ 0 \end{array}$$

(3)
$$\begin{array}{r} 0.\ 1\ 6 \\ \times\ 0.\ 2\ 1 \\ \hline 1\ 6 \\ 3\ 2\ \ \\ \hline 3\ 3\ 6 \end{array}$$

2 Based on the product in the first column, write the products in the other columns.

Factor	4.8	4.8	4.8	4.8	4.8
Factor	15	1.5	1	0.15	0.015
Product	72				

Observing the table above, what can be found? Please fill in the brackets. When one factor equals 4.8, if the other factor is greater than 1, then the product is (   ) 4.8; if the other factor equals 1, then the product is (   ) 4.8; if the other factor is less than 1, then the product is (   ) 4.8.

3 Without calculating, fill in the ○ with ">", "<" or "=".

(1) 2.56×12.8 ○ 2.56　　(2) 7.95×0.8 ○ 7.95

(3) 0.78×12.7 ○ 12.7　　(4) 1.003×0.9 ○ 0.9

(5) 0.95×0.98 ○ 0.95×1.02　　(6) 4.75×12 ○ 4.75×1.2

(7) 0.78×2.7 ○ 7.8×0.27　　(8) 4.6×0.1 ○ $4.6 \div 10$

4 Use the column method to calculate.

(1) $1.28 \times 0.35 =$　　(2) $5.26 \times 2.04 =$

(3) $3.32 \times 0.045 =$　　　　　　(4) $3.02 \times 0.016 =$

(5) $0.45 \times 0.504 =$　　　　　　(6) $2020 \times 1.28 =$

5 Multiple choice questions.

(1) In the following expressions, the product that is less than 36.5 is (　　).

(A) 36.5×2.54　　　　(B) 25.4×36.5

(C) 36.5×0.254　　　　(D) 36.5×1

(2) If $0.24 \times M < 0.24$, then M (　　) 1.

(A) $<$　　(B) $=$　　(C) $>$　　(D) uncertain

(3) The product of Number A and Number B is greater than Number A and Number B. Then Number A is a (　　) and Number B is a (　　).

(A) pure decimal, mixed decimal

(B) mixed decimal, pure decimal

(C) pure decimal, pure decimal

(D) mixed decimal, mixed decimal

(4) Given two pure decimals, comparing their sum and their product, the result is that the sum (　　) the product.

(A) $<$　　(B) $=$　　(C) $>$　　(D) uncertain

6 Application problems.

(1) One kilogram of apples costs 3.2 yuan. How much does one need to pay to buy 1.4 kilograms of apples?

(2) A school organised its pupils to collect old newspapers to donate to "Hope schools". There were 6 classes in Grade 5. Each class collected 48.65 kilograms of old newspapers on average. How many kilograms of old newspapers did Grade 5 pupils collect altogether? If the price for the old newspapers was 0.8 yuan per kilogram, how much money would the pupils in Grade 5 donate in total?

Enhancement and extension

7. Find the calculation pattern of the number sentences on the left side first, and then follow the pattern to find the results of the number sentences on the right side.

Since $2.4 \times 2.6 = 6.24$, we get $1.3 \times 1.7 =$ (   );
$5.5 \times 5.5 = 30.25$, $4.1 \times 4.9 =$ (   );
$8.1 \times 8.9 = 72.09$, $6.2 \times 6.8 =$ (   );
$9.2 \times 9.8 = 90.16$, $7.4 \times 7.6 =$ (   );
$10.3 \times 10.7 = 110.21$, $15.5 \times 15.5 =$ (   ).

2.6 Multiplying three numbers, and mixed operations of multiplication with addition and subtraction

Basic questions

1 Combine the following number sentences for separate steps into one mixed number sentence.

(1) $6.2-2.6=3.6$

$2.5\times3.6=9$

____

(2) $0.45\times1.2=0.54$

$3.4\times0.54=1.836$

____

2 Work these out step by step.

(1) $4.81\times0.5\times3$

(2) $13.78-1.03\times4.2$

(3) $0.18\times(8.14-3.64)$

(4) $0.81\times50\times0.07$

(5) $12.49-0.48\times3.5+6.3$

(6) $0.75\times1.4\times420$

3 Write the number sentences and then calculate.

(1) The sum of 7.8 and 0.7 is multiplied by 0.6. What is the product?

(2) The number that is 0.4 less than 3.2 is multiplied by 3.9. What is the product?

(3) How much more is 10 times 0.44 than 2.5?

(4) Number A is 6.9, which is 0.9 more than twice Number B. What is Number B?

4 Application problems.

(1) To make one set of children's clothes, it needs 2.08 metres of cloth; to make one set of adult clothes, it needs 2.5 times as much. To make one set each of children's clothes and adult clothes, how many metres of cloth are needed in total?

(2) One iron rod is 6.4 metres long. It weighs 4.9 kilograms per metre. How much do 70 such iron rods weigh in kilograms? How much is this in tonnes?

(3) Xiao Pang used 40 yuan to buy eight 0.25-litre bottles of Sprite at 3.20 yuan per bottle. How much change should he get?

(4) A square has a side length of 0.6 decimetres. Four such squares are combined to make up one large square. What are the perimeter and the area of the large square?

Enhancement and extension

5 Insert brackets in the following number sentences to make the equations true.

(1) $15.2 + 2.5 \times 3 - 10.6 = 42.5$

(2) $30 - 1.8 \times 2.6 - 1.5 = 26.82$

(3) $4.5 \times 5.3 - 2.5 + 1.8 = 19.55$

2.7 Extending laws of multiplication with whole numbers to decimals

Basic questions

1 Draw lines to match the calculations with the same answers on both the left and the right sides.

3.6×5.4	$0.8 \times 1.25 + 0.8 \times 12.5$
$4.6 \times 1.9 + 5.4 \times 1.9$	$6.7 \times (4 \times 2.5)$
$0.8 \times (1.25 + 12.5)$	$(4.6 + 5.4) \times 1.9$
$6.7 \times 4 \times 2.5$	5.4×3.6

2 Are the following calculations correct? Put a "√" for correct and a "×" for incorrect in the (   ).

(1) $9.9 \times 0.59 = (9.9 + 0.1) \times 0.59$ (   )

(2) $12.5 \times 8.8 = 12.5 \times 8 \times 12.5 \times 0.8$ (   )

(3) $10.2 \times 2.7 - 0.54 = 2.7 \times (10.2 - 0.2)$ (   )

(4) $12.5 \times 2.4 = (12.5 \times 8) \times 3$ (   )

3 Calculate the following in whatever ways that are simple and convenient.

(1) $12.5 \times 3.2 \times 0.8$

(2) 7.2×0.25

(3) 0.99×10.1

(4) $6.4 \times 4.6 + 6.4 \times 5.4 - 6.4$

(5) $7.2 \times 0.125 \times 1.1$

(6) $(6.2 \times 6.8 + 1.8 \times 6.8) \times 1.25$

(7) $(2.5+2.5+2.5+2.5+2.5)\times 88$

(8) $7.8\times 0.37+0.78\times 6.3$

(9) $5.4\times 3.8-6.5\times 4.4+2.7\times 5.4$

4 Application problems.

(1) In a set of school uniform, the jacket costs 121.5 yuan and the trousers cost 78.5 yuan. How much do 320 sets of such school uniforms cost?

(2) One water pump can pump 12.5 tonnes of water in one hour. At this rate, how many tonnes of water in total will 16 such water pumps pump in 2.5 hours?

(3) The floor of the lounge of Xiao Pang's home is covered with a total of 240 square tiles with side length 0.25 metres. How many square metres is the area of the lounge of Xiao Pang's home?

Enhancement and extension

5 Calculate using a simple and convenient way: $2.22\times 6.66+3.33\times 5.55$.

2.8 Division of decimals by whole numbers (1)

Basic questions

1 Fill in the boxes.

(1) 8.4÷6=□

8.4 is □ times 0.1.

84÷6=□

□ times 0.1 is □.

(2) 9.38÷7=□

9.38 is □ times 0.01.

938÷□=134

□ times 0.01 is □.

2 Following the example, calculate.

(1) 19.6÷14 =

19.6 is 196 times 0.1.

```
      1 4
    ______
14 ) 1 9 6
     1 4
    ______
       5 6
       5 6
    ______
         0
```

14 times 0.1 is □.

(2) 26.1÷9 =

(3) 41.04÷12 =

3 Use the column method to calculate.

(1) 43.2÷4 =

(2) 115.2÷18 =

(3) 408.8÷73 =

(4) 38.22÷7 =

(5) 313.6÷49 =

(6) 99.32÷13 =

4 Write the number sentences and then calculate.

(1) 6 times a number is 128. 4. What is the number?

(2) Number A is 22. 8. Number A is 12 times Number B. What is the difference between the two numbers A and B?

5 Application problems.

(1) Xiao Ming's mum bought 3 kilograms of apples for 7. 35 yuan. How much did one kilogram of apples cost?

(2) A vehicle travelled from place A to place B in 3. 6 hours at a speed of 48 kilometres per hour. The return trip took 4 hours. How many kilometres per hour did it travel on the way back?

Enhancement and extension

6 A piece of wire can be bent into a rectangle 1. 6 metres long and 1. 2 metres wide. If it is bent into a square, then what is the area of the square?

2.9 Division of decimals by whole numbers (2)

Basic questions

1. Work these out mentally and write down the answers.

6.9 ÷ 3 =　　8.4 ÷ 4 =　　44.8 ÷ 7 =　　59.4 ÷ 9 =

7.2 ÷ 6 =　　9.5 ÷ 5 =　　11.8 ÷ 2 =　　8.68 ÷ 7 =

2. Complete the working of the calculation.

□ / 5)0. 9 5 → 0 / 5)0. 9 5 → 0. 1□ / 5)0. 9 5 / 5 / 4 5······meaning 45 times □ / 4 5 / 0

The whole number part of the dividend is less than the divisor. The ones place of the quotient should be □.

The decimal point in the quotient must be aligned with the decimal point in the □.

The method is the same as for the division of whole numbers.

3. Use the column method to calculate.

(1) 6.64 ÷ 8 =　　(2) 7.95 ÷ 15 =　　(3) 1.248 ÷ 26 =

(4) 8.64 ÷ 36 =　　(5) 0.112 ÷ 7 =　　(6) 1.11 ÷ 37 =

4. Write the number sentences and then calculate.

(1) 25 times a number is 12.5. What is the number?

(2) The difference between 53. 8 and 53. 26 is divided by 54. What is the quotient?

5 Application problems.

(1) An elephant weighs 9. 9 tonnes, 18 times the weight of a horse. What is the weight of the horse?

(2) Two road maintenance teams A and B were each building a road. Team A built 3. 45 metres of road in 5 days and team B built 5. 04 metres of road in 7 days. Which team had a better work efficiency?

(3) A sugar refinery produced 3. 25 tonnes of sugar by using 25 tonnes of sugar cane. How many tonnes of sugar can be produced from every tonne of sugar cane on average? Based on this calculation, how many tonnes of sugar can be produced from 40. 5 tonnes of sugar cane?

(4) The area of a rectangular flowerbed is 2. 4 square metres. Given the length of the flowerbed is 3 metres, find the width and the perimeter of the flowerbed.

Enhancement and extension

6 The sum of Number A and Number B is 8. 36. If the decimal point of Number A is moved one place to right, it will be equal to Number B. What are Number A and Number B?

2.10 Division of decimals by whole numbers (3)

Basic questions

1 A 1.5 litre bottle of juice is shared equally by 5 people. How many litres of juice does each person get? If it is shared by 4 people, then how much does each person get?

$1.5 \div 5 = \square$ $\qquad\qquad$ $1.5 \div 4 = \square$

```
                          0. 3 □ □
                        ┌─────────
5 ) 1. 5              4 ) 1. 5
                          1  2
                          ─────
                             3 □
                           □ □
                          ───────
                             □ □
                             □ □
                          ───────
                               0
```

2 Use the column method to calculate.

(1) $7.8 \div 4 =$ $\qquad$ (2) $26.1 \div 6 =$ $\qquad$ (3) $5.1 \div 60 =$

(4) $0.9 \div 30 =$ $\qquad$ (5) $5.98 \div 52 =$ $\qquad$ (6) $4.2 \div 24 =$

3 Write the number sentences and then calculate.

(1) What is the quotient of 1.8 divided by 4?

(2) Eight times a number is 10.8. What is 10 times the number?

4 Application problems.

(1) A clothes shop used 56.4 metres of cloth to make 24 sets of clothes of the same size. How many metres of cloth were used to make a set of clothes on average?

(2) A 2.2-metre-long wire is used to form a square. What is the side length of the square? What is the area of the square?

(3) One box of Danish cookies weighs 500 grams and costs 28.8 yuan, while one can of European continental cookies weighs 800 grams and costs 38.8 yuan. Which type of cookies is cheaper?

(4) A kindergarten bought 32.6 kilograms of apples, which was 1.4 kilograms more than 5 times the weight of the oranges it bought. How many kilograms of oranges did it buy?

Enhancement and extension

5 During the "1st October" Golden Week, many supermarkets offer promotions. For a soft drink in 2 litre bottles, the price Aunt Li paid was 5.45 yuan per bottle, while the price Aunt Zhang paid was 7.1 yuan per bottle, but with a promotion of buying 3 and getting 1 free. If Aunt Zhang and Aunt Li each needed to buy 4 bottles of the drink, can you work out who had a better deal, Aunt Zhang or Aunt Li? How many methods do you have?

2.11 Division of decimals by whole numbers (4)

Basic questions

1 Based on $54 \div 24 = 2.25$, work out mentally and write down the quotients of the following divisions.

$0.54 \div 24 = (\quad)$ $5400 \div 24 = (\quad)$ $540 \div 24 = (\quad)$

$5.4 \div 24 = (\quad)$ $0.0054 \div 24 = (\quad)$ $0.054 \div 24 = (\quad)$

2 Use the column method to calculate.

(1) $36 \div 90 =$ (2) $8 \div 32 =$ (3) $10 \div 125 =$

(4) $27 \div 72 =$ (5) $1 \div 16 =$ (6) $34 \div 8 =$

3 Write the number sentences and then calculate.

(1) How many times 26 is 65?

(2) The product of 3 and 0.5 is divided by 12. What is the quotient?

4 Application problems.

(1) Xiao Pang walked 1.5 kilometres in 15 minutes. How many kilometres could he walk in 1 minute?

(2) The height of the Xinming Mansion is 180 metres, and the height of the Oriental Pearl TV Tower is 486 metres. How many times the height of the Xinming Mansion is that of the Oriental Pearl TV Tower?

(3) A vehicle travelled 309 kilometres in 4 hours. How many kilometres did the vehicle travel each hour on average?

(4) Xiao Qiao bought 9 copies of an exercise book and Xiao Ya bought 5 copies of the same exercise book. Xiao Ya spent 31 yuan less than Xiao Qiao. How much did each copy of the exercise book cost? How much did they spend in total?

Enhancement and extension

5. 150 pupils from Grade 5 in a school went on a trip to visit a science and technology museum. The admission ticket was 30 yuan per person, and the insurance fee was 2.75 yuan per person. Three coaches were hired at the cost of 1440 yuan per coach. What was the average cost of the visit per pupil?

6. There is a mixed decimal. If the decimal part is increased to 3 times its value, then the result is 6.2; if the decimal part is increased to 8 times its value, then the result is 8.2. Find the mixed decimal.

2.12 Division by a decimal number (1)

Basic questions

1 Fill in the brackets with the correct numbers.

5.87 ÷ 0.025 = ( ) ÷ 25　　0.9 ÷ 0.04 = ( ) ÷ 4

1.378 ÷ 1.5 = ( ) ÷ 15　　475 ÷ 0.29 = ( ) ÷ 29

2 Based on 32 ÷ 12.5 = 2.56, work out mentally and write down the quotients of the following questions.

32 ÷ 1.25 = ( )　0.32 ÷ 0.125 = ( )　32 ÷ 0.125 = ( )

0.32 ÷ 1.25 = ( )　3.2 ÷ 0.125 = ( )　0.032 ÷ 0.125 = ( )

3 Let's have a try.

7 ÷ 1.4 = □　　6 ÷ 0.12 = □　　0.091 ÷ 0.005 = □

↓×10 ↓×10 ↑　　↓×( ) ↓×( ) ↑　　↓×( ) ↓×( ) ↑

70 ÷ 14 = □　　□ ÷ □ = □　　□ ÷ □ = □

4 Draw lines to match the divisions with the same answers on both the left and the right sides.

(1) $8.9\overline{)382.7}$　　(A) $89\overline{)382.7}$

(2) $8.9\overline{)38\,270}$　　(B) $89\overline{)38\,270}$

(3) $0.89\overline{)382.7}$　　(C) $89\overline{)3827}$

(4) $8.9\overline{)38.27}$　　(D) $89\overline{)382\,700}$

5 Use the column method to calculate.

(1) 2.05 ÷ 20.5 =　　(2) 10.2 ÷ 0.24 =　　(3) 6 ÷ 7.5 =

(4) $3.658 \div 6.2 =$　　(5) $0.324 \div 0.18 =$　　(6) $0.7 \div 0.035 =$

6 Application problems.

(1) A 40-metre-long wire is cut into pieces that are each 2.5 metres long. Into how many pieces will it be cut?

(2) A clothing factory made 76.8 thousand sets of clothes in the first half of this year, which was 1.6 times the production of the second half of the year. How many thousand sets of clothes did this factory make this year in total?

(3) A car travelled for 2.5 hours from place A to place B, which were 207.9 kilometres apart. It took 0.2 hours more on the return trip. How many kilometres per hour did the car travel on the way back?

Enhancement and extension

7 The quotient of Number A divided by Number B is 0.3. The sum of Number A and Number B is 2.08. What are Number A and Number B?

2.13 Division by a decimal number (2)

Basic questions

1 Observe carefully and complete the table quickly.

Dividend	1.2				
Divisor	0.015	0.15	1	1.5	15
Quotient					

By observing the table above, what did you find? Please fill in the brackets. When the dividend equals 1.2, if the divisor is greater than 1, then the quotient is (　　　) 1.2; if the divisor equals 1, then the quotient is (　　　) 1.2; if the divisor is less than 1, then the quotient is (　　　) 1.2.

2 Without calculating, fill in the ○ with ">", "<" or "=".

(1) $12.1 \div 1.1$ ○ 12.1　　(2) $10.8 \div 0.9$ ○ 10.8

(3) $0.36 \div 0.9$ ○ 0.36　　(4) $2.97 \div 0.99$ ○ 2.97

(5) $8.9 \div 1.25$ ○ 8.9　　(6) $7.8 \div 3.9$ ○ $0.78 \div 0.39$

(7) 3.8×10 ○ $3.8 \div 0.1$　　(8) 7.2×0.9 ○ $7.2 \div 0.9$

3 Use the column method to calculate. (Check the answers to the questions marked with *)

(1) $3.8 \div 0.4 =$　　(2) $2 \div 2.5 =$

(3) $22.1 \div 0.17 =$　　*(4) $0.216 \div 0.72 =$

(5) $6.24 \div 0.26 =$

* (6) $0.303 \div 0.025 =$

4 Work these out step by step.

(1) $2.4 \div 0.8 \times 0.9$

(2) $35.65 \div 4.6 \times 1.3$

(3) $0.58 \times 4.3 \div 0.2$

(4) $20.36 \div 0.4 \div 0.5$

5 Multiple choice questions

(1) In the following division sentences, the one with the quotient greater than the dividend is (　　).

① $8.2 \div 4.1$　② $1.25 \div 25$　③ $0.36 \div 0.8$　④ $10.8 \div 3.6$

(A) ①　(B) ②　(C) ③　(D) ④

(2) For $1.17 \div 0.9$, the quotient obtained must be (　　).

(A) greater than 1.17　(B) equal to 1.17

(C) less than 1.17　(D) less than 1

(3) Without calculating for the four divisions ① $8.256 \div 2.14$, ② $8256 \div 2.14$, ③ $82.56 \div 0.214$, ④ $0.8256 \div 0.0214$, the order of the quotients should be (　　).

(A) ②>③>④>①　(B) ②>③>①>④

(C) ③>②>④>①　(D) ③>②>①>④

(4) Given $M > 0$, the incorrect number sentence of the following is (　　).

(A) $M \div 0.1 > M$　(B) $M \times 1.1 > M$

(C) $M \div 1.1 > M$　(D) $M \times 0.99 < M$

(5) When $1.08 \div N > 1.08$, the correct statement of the following is (　　).

(A) $N > 1$　(B) $0 < N \leqslant 1$　(C) $N = 1$　(D) $0 < N < 1$

(6) When $7.2 \times E \leqslant 7.2 \div E$, E must be ( ).

(A) greater than 1, but less than 7.2

(B) greater than 0, but less than or equal to 1

(C) greater than or equal to 1, but less than 7.2

(D) greater than 0, but less than 1

Enhancement and extension

6 Number A is $0.\underbrace{0\cdots0}_{24\text{ zeros}}24$, and Number B is $0.\underbrace{0\cdots0}_{25\text{ zeros}}125$. Find the quotient of Number A divided by Number B.

2.14 Division by a decimal number (3)

Basic questions

1. Work these out mentally and write down the answers.

$12 \div 1.2 =$ $\quad$ $3.5 \div 0.5 =$ $\quad$ $0.48 \div 24 =$

$0.49 \div 0.7 =$ $\quad$ $2.68 \div 0.4 =$ $\quad$ $1.25 \div 2.5 =$

2. Use the column method to calculate. (Check the answers to the questions marked with *)

(1) $0.084 \div 0.24 =$

(2) $1.62 \div 4.5 =$

(3) $138.6 \div 2.2 =$

*(4) $2.754 \div 2.7 =$

(5) $0.5852 \div 0.19 =$

*(6) $6.75 \div 0.018 =$

3. Fill in the spaces.

(1) The quotient of $2.7 \div 0.6$ is 4, the remainder is (　　　　).

(2) For $0.64 \div 0.37$, when the quotient is a whole number, the remainder is (　　　　); when the quotient has one decimal place, the remainder is (　　　　); when the quotient has two decimal places, the remainder is (　　　　).

(3) Fill in the ◯ with "$<$", "$>$" or "$=$".

$78 \div 0.9$ ◯ $78 \div 1.1$ $\quad$ $26.25 \div 1.05$ ◯ 26.25×1.05

1.6×100 ◯ $1.6 \div 0.01$ $\quad$ $4.8 \div 1.4$ ◯ $2.4 \div 0.7$

4 Multiple choice questions.

(1) In $0.753 \div 0.13$, when the quotient is 5.7, the remainder is (　　).

(A) 12　　(B) 1.2　　(C) 0.12　　(D) 0.012

(2) If $a \times 0.9 = b \div 0.9 = c \div 1$ (a, b and c are all greater than 0), then the relationships between the three numbers a, b and c are (　　).

(A) $a > b > c$　(B) $a > c > b$　(C) $b > c > a$　(D) $c > b > a$

5 Application problems.

(1) A 18.6-metre-long rope is cut into short pieces that are each 2.5 metres long. What is the greatest number of pieces it can be cut into? How many metres long is the remaining part?

(2) 29 litres of drink are poured into 1.25 litre bottles. How many bottles can be filled up? How many litres of drink will be left over?

(3) There is a type of water pen that sells for 2.6 yuan each. Xiao Dingding has 10 yuan to spend on the pens. What is the greatest number of pens he could buy? How much change would he get?

(4) A car park charges at least 5 yuan per entry. After 2 hours, an additional 2.5 yuan is charged for every additional hour. Mr Wang parked his car in the car park one time and paid 20 yuan before exiting. How many hours did he park his car?

Enhancement and extension

6 There is a division sentence: $11.9 \div (\quad) = (\quad) \cdots\cdots 1.1$. When the quotient is a whole number, how many different numbers could the divisor be? What are these numbers?

2.15 Recurring decimals

Basic questions

1 Observing the following numbers carefully, which are recurring decimals? Express these numbers using a simple way.

(1) 2.999…(　　　　)　　(2) 2.222 222(　　　　)

(3) 4.1333…(　　　　)　　(4) 5.125 121 2…(　　　　)

(5) 0.647 746…(　　　　)　　(6) 6.416 416…(　　　　)

(7) 5.027 27…(　　　　)　　(8) 7.019 201 920…(　　　　)

(9) 10.020 020 002…(　　　　)

2 Use the column method to calculate. If the quotient is a recurring decimal, express it in a simple way.

(1) $2 \div 9 =$　　(2) $9 \div 5.5 =$　　(3) $58.6 \div 11 =$

3 Fill in the ○ with ">", "<" or "=".

$3.\dot{1}\dot{4}$ ○ $3.1\dot{4}$　　$8.\dot{6}$ ○ $8.\dot{5}\dot{9}$　　2.1414… ○ 2.144…

$0.\dot{3}$ ○ $1 \div 3$　　5.666 ○ 5.666…　　$1.\dot{2}\dot{7}$ ○ 1.2727…

$4 \div 9$ ○ 0.4　　3.22… ○ $3.\dot{2}$

4 True or false. (Put a "√" for true and a "×" for false.)

(1) 8.141 414 14 is a recurring decimal.　(　　)

(2) $0.100\,100\,10\cdots = 0.\dot{1}00\dot{1}$.　(　　)

(3) $0.\dot{6} = 0.\dot{6}\dot{0}$.　(　　)

(4) $4 \div 6 \approx 0.\dot{6}$.　(　　)

(5) $5.624\,524\,5\cdots = 5.6\dot{2}4\dot{5}$.　(　　)

5 Put the four numbers $1.12\dot{1}$, $1.1\dot{2}\dot{1}$, 1.121 and $1.\dot{1}2\dot{1}$ in order from the greatest to the least.

____

6 Multiple choice questions.

(1) Among the following decimals, the one that can be expressed with a recurring period is (　　).

(A) 4.166 66　　(B) 5.023 232 3

(C) 8.980 808 0…　　(D) 3.141 592 6

(2) 0.060 808… expressed in a simple way is (　　).

(A) $0.\dot{0}60\dot{8}$　　(B) $0.0\dot{6}0\dot{8}$

(C) $0.06\dot{0}\dot{8}$　　(D) $0.0608\dot{0}\dot{8}$

(3) Putting the numbers $0.8\dot{3}\dot{4}$, $0.\dot{8}3\dot{4}$, 0.834 and $0.83\dot{4}$ in order from the greatest to the least, the number in the second place is (　　).

(A) $0.8\dot{3}\dot{4}$　　(B) $0.\dot{8}3\dot{4}$

(C) 0.834　　(D) $0.83\dot{4}$

7 In a vegetable wholesale market, the price for cabbage is 2.60 yuan per kilogram. If a purchase is over 50 kilograms, then it can be sold at half price (wholesale price). A school canteen bought 85 kilograms of cabbage. How much did the school actually save?

Enhancement and extension

8 Calculate: $0.\dot{1}+0.0\dot{1}+0.00\dot{1}+0.000\dot{1}+0.0000\dot{1}=$ (　　　).

9 In calculation $4\div7$, the digit in the tenth place in the quotient after the decimal point is (　　　). The sum of the first 100 digits in the quotient after the decimal point is (　　　).

2.16 Calculation with calculators

Basic questions

1 Use the column method to calculate first, and then check the answers with a calculator.

(1) $4.38 \times 65.24 =$

(2) $0.978 \times 36.7 =$

(3) $96.32 \times 16.5 =$

(4) $934.72 \div 25.4 =$

(5) $298.792 \div 67.6 =$

(6) $443.7 \div 1.45 =$

2 Use a calculator to work out questions ②—④, and then use reasoning to find the answers to questions ⑤ and ⑥.

① $6 \times 6 =$

② $66 \times 66 =$

③ $666 \times 666 =$

④ $6666 \times 6666 =$

⑤ $66\,666 \times 66\,666 =$

⑥ $666\,666 \times 666\,666 =$

3 Use a calculator to investigate.

(1) $1 \div 9 =$

(2) $2 \div 9 =$

(3) $3 \div 9 =$

(4) $4 \div 9 =$

(5) $5 \div 9 =$

(6) $6 \div 9 =$

(7) $7 \div 9 =$

(8) $8 \div 9 =$

4 Application problems.

(1) The Shenzhou VI spacecraft flew in a circular orbit in space. One round of the circular orbit is about 42 371 kilometres long. It took the spacecraft 90 minutes to fly one round along the orbit. How many kilometres did the Shenzhou VI spacecraft fly per second? (Use a calculator to calculate)

(2) According to available statistics, an untightened water tap leaks about 0.018 tonnes of water in a day.

① According to this, how many tonnes of water are wasted in one year (take one year as 365 days)?

② If that amount of water is filled into drinking water barrels (each with a capacity of about 19 kilograms of water), what is the maximum number of barrels it could fill up?

③ A household uses 3 barrels of water each month. How many months could the amount of water be used? About how many years is it?

Enhancement and extension

5 Use a calculator to find the answers to the first four questions, find the pattern, and then write the answers to the remaining questions.

(1) $12\ 345\ 679 \times 1 \times 9 =$

(2) $12\ 345\ 679 \times 2 \times 9 =$

(3) $12\ 345\ 679 \times 3 \times 9 =$

(4) $12\ 345\ 679 \times 4 \times 9 =$

(5) $12\ 345\ 679 \times 5 \times 9 =$

(6) $12\ 345\ 679 \times 6 \times 9 =$

(7) $12\ 345\ 679 \times 7 \times 9 =$

(8) $12\ 345\ 679 \times 8 \times 9 =$

(9) $12\ 345\ 679 \times 9 \times 9 =$

2.17 Approximation of products and quotients

Basic questions

1 Fill in the table.

	Round to the nearest one	Round to the nearest tenth	Round to the nearest hundredth
3.409			
16.032			
5.697			
29.993			

2 Use the column method to calculate.

7.54×4.8
(to the nearest tenth)

0.345×0.81
(to the nearest thousandth)

$6.34 \div 2.56$
(to the nearest hundredth)

$36.32 \div 0.62$
(to the nearest tenth)

6.34×2.56
(to the nearest thousandth)

$21.63 \div 6.3$
(to the nearest hundredth)

3 Application problems.

(1) Xiao Ya wanted to buy some fruit in a fruit store. The price for apples was 6.56 yuan per kilogram. She bought 2.4 kilograms of apples. How much should she pay?

(2) An oil bottle can be filled up at most with 4.5 litres. There are 60 litres of oil to fill up. How many such bottles are needed?

(3) On 8th March 2012, Women's Day, Xiao Ya's aunt sent her a book from the United Sates. The price of the book was 4.5 US dollars. How much was it equivalent to in Chinese yuan? (Use a calculator to calculate)

Bank of China	
1 US dollar to Chinese yuan:	6.3018
1 euros to Chinese yuan:	8.4016
1 HK dollar to Chinese yuan:	0.812 51
1 British pound to Chinese yuan:	10.0356
100 Japanese yen to Chinese yuan:	7.7630
	8th March 2012

(4) On 8th March, Mum wanted to exchange 8000 Chinese yuan into euros. How many euros could she get? (Use a calculator to calculate)

(5) On a certain day, the exchange rate at the Bank of China was: 1 British pound could be exchanged into 10.0356 Chinese yuan. Then how many Bristish pounds could 10 000 Chinese yuan be exchanged into? (Use a calculator to calculate)

Enhancement and extension

4 On 3rd November 2006 Mr Li exchanged 1000 Chinese yuan into US dollars (1 US dollar could be exchanged into 7.7386 Chinese yuan). On 8th March 2012, Mr Li exchanged these dollars into Chinese yuan. Did Mr Li earn or lose money? If he earned, how much was the gain? If he lost, how much was the loss?

2.18 Practice and exercise

Basic questions

1 Use the laws of operations to fill in each $\square$ below with a suitable number and the $\bigcirc$ with a suitable operation sign.

(1) $\square \times 0.84 = \square \times 0.7$

(2) $\square \times (3.28 \times 0.8) = (12.5 \times 0.8) \times \square$

(3) $\square \times (0.125 + 2.5) = \square \times \square \bigcirc \square \times 4$

2 Use the column method to calculate. (Check the answer to the question marked with *)

(1) 0.09×0.247

(2) $13.6 \div 2.7$
(Round to the nearest tenth)

*(3) $8.84 \div 1.7$

3 Combine the following number sentences with separate steps into one mixed number sentence.

(1) $60.8 \div 16 = 3.8$
$13.5 - 3.8 = 9.7$

____

(2) $4.25 + 5.8 = 10.05$
$1.4 \times 10.05 = 14.07$

____

4 Work these out step by step. (Calculate smartly if possible.)

(1) $8.1 \div 0.25$

(2) $9.18 - 9.18 \div 9 \times 2.9$

(3) $18.7-8.7\div 2.5$

(4) $7.8\div(0.39\div 5)$

(5) $87.25-(7.25+4.83+5.17)$

(6) $43.2\div 8\times 12.5$

(7) $19.5\times 5.8+5.2\times 19.5-19.5$

5 Write the number sentences and then calculate.

(1) 27.8 is divided by the difference between 19.3 and 16.52. What is the result?

(2) Number A is 3.6, which is 4.4 less than 4 times Number B. What is Number B?

6 Application problems.

(1) Fill 38 litres of drink into bottles, each with a capacity of 1.25 litres. At most how many bottles can it fill up? How many litres will be left over?

(2) It took a pigeon 0.7 hours to fly 9.1 kilometres. Based on this speed, how much time would it take the pigeon to fly 13.91 kilometres?

(3) A batch of coal was delivered to a canteen. It was planned to use 10.5 kilograms of coal each day and last 8 days. It actually lasted 10 days. How many fewer kilograms of the coal were used per day than planned?

(4) A beekeeper collected 73.8 kilograms of honey from 36 beehives. According to this, how many kilograms of honey can be collected from 72 beehives?

(5) A rectangular billboard is 8.1 metres long and 2.5 metres wide. If each kilogram of paint can be used to cover 4.5 square metres of the board, then how many kilograms of the paint is needed to cover both sides of the billboard?

7 Fill in the brackets.

(1) The decimal point of a number was first moved three places to the left and then moved two places to the right. The resulting number is 4.4. The original number was (   ).

(2) 1.110 101 01⋯ is a recurring decimal. It is written as (   ) in a simple way. Rounding it down to two decimal places, the result is (   ).

(3) Put the five numbers 5.91, 5.9, $5.\dot{9}$, 5.912 and 5.912 912 in order from the least to the greatest. The number in the second place is (   ).

(4) Without calculating, fill in the ◯ with "$>$", "$<$" or "$=$".

7.8×1.4 ◯ 7.8×0.4 $\qquad$ $5.6\div0.5$ ◯ $56\div5$

$3.13\div9.1$ ◯ $3.13\div1.9$ $\qquad$ 5.4 ◯ 5.4×0.72

0.97×1.05 ◯ $0.97\div1.05$ $\qquad$ $2.6\div3.01$ ◯ 2.6

$9.9\div0.9$ ◯ 9.9×0.9 $\qquad$ $3.16\div0.11$ ◯ $3.6\div1.1$

(5) When a decimal number with three decimal places was rounded off, it is 4.90. The least value of the number could be (   ), and its greatest value could be (   ).

(6) When the quotient of $64.4\div4.3$ is 14.9, the remainder is (   ).

8 Multiple choice questions.

(1) If $0<a<b<1$, then the quotient of $a\div b$ must be (   ).

(A) <0 $\qquad$ (B) $<a$

(C) $>a$ $\qquad$ (D) All the above three answers are possible

(2) If $a\div0.8=b\div1$ (both a and b are greater than 0), then a (   ) b.

(A) $>$ $\qquad$ (B) $<$ $\qquad$ (C) $=$ $\qquad$ (D) uncertain

(3) Among the following equations, the one that leads to $a<1$ is (   ).

(A) $a\div0.1=1$ $\qquad$ (B) $a\times0.8=1$

(C) $6.3\div a=1$ $\qquad$ (D) $0.8\times a=1$

(4) In the four numbers 0.707, $0.\dot{7}0\dot{7}$, $0.7\dot{0}\dot{7}$ and $0.70\dot{7}$, the greatest number is (   )

(A) 0.707 $\qquad$ (B) $0.\dot{7}0\dot{7}$ $\qquad$ (C) $0.7\dot{0}\dot{7}$ $\qquad$ (D) $0.70\dot{7}$

9 True or false. (Put a "$\surd$" for true and a "$\times$" for false)

(1) 9.373 737 is a recurring decimal. (   )

(2) When rounding off is used, the meaning of 3.6 and that of 3.60 are different. (   )

Enhancement and extension

10 The sum of A and B is 6.55, the sum of A and C is 7.55 and the sum of B and C is 7.1. What are A, B, and C?

Unit test 2

A. Calculation. (44 marks in total)

1 Work these out mentally and write down the answers. (4 marks in total)

(1) $5 \times 2.4 =$ (2) $4.7 \div 2.5 =$

(3) $2.8 + 7.2 \times 0.1 =$ (4) $9.9 - 4.5 \div 0.9 =$

2 Use the column method to calculate. (Check the answer to the question marked with *) (16 marks in total)

*(1) $10.056 \div 2.4$ (2) 3.7×1.28

(3) $7.5 \div 1.7$
(Give the quotient to two decimal places)

(4) $7 \div 18$
(Use a recurring decimal to express the quotient)

3 Work these out step by step. (Calculate smartly if possible) (16 marks in total)

(1) $7.2 \times 2.5 + 7.2 \times 7.4 + 0.72$ (2) $8 \times (125 \times 0.125)$

(3) $4.8 \times (90.2 - 13.2)$ (4) $[3.72 - 0.72 \times (1.6 + 2.4)] \div 0.1$

4 Write the number sentences and then calculate. (8 marks in total)

(1) Number A is 4.8, which is 0.6 greater than 4 times Number B. What is Number B?

(2) The product of 1.5 and 0.24 is divided by the sum of 2.85 and 0.75. What is the quotient?

B. Application problems. (36 marks in total)

5 A vehicle travelled from place A to place B at a speed of 85 kilometres per hour on average. After 2.4 hours, it arrived at place B. On the way back, it travelled at a speed of 80 kilometres per hour on average. How many hours would it take to get back to place A?

6 A construction team planned to repair 300 metres of a road each day and complete it in 25 days. Now the plan needs to be brought forward so it will be completed in 15 days. How many more metres of the road needs to be repaired each day than originally planned?

7 Every 1.25 litres of drink can fill up a bottle. Now there are 9.6 litres of drink. How many such bottles can it fill up? How many litres will be left over?

8 A barrel of coal oil weighed 8 kilograms, inclusive of the weight of the barrel. After half of the oil was used, it weighed 4.5 kilograms, again inclusive of the weight of the barrel. What was the weight of the barrel?

9 A rectangular lawn is 13.5 metres long. Its perimeter is exactly equal to the perimeter of a square lawn with a side length of 9 metres. How many times the width is the length of the rectangular lawn?

10 One of the rooms in Xiao Pang's home is 4.2 metres long and 3.8 metres wide. The floor is to be tiled with square tiles of side 0.2 metres. What is the minimum number of such tiles should be purchased?

C. Concepts. (20 marks in total)

(A) Fill in the brackets. (15 marks in total)

11 Based on $6.75 \div 5.4 = 1.25$, use reasoning to get the answers to the following questions.

(1) $67.5 \div 54 =$ (　　　　)　　(2) $675 \div 0.54 =$ (　　　　)

(3) $12.5 \times 0.054 =$ (　　　　)

12 Fill in the (　　　) with ">", "<" or "=".

(1) 5.76×1.87 (　　　) 5.76　　(2) 9.35×0.72 (　　　) 9.35

(3) $7.2 \div 0.1$ (　　　) 7.2×0.1

13 Use a recurring period to express each of the following decimals.

(1) 3.146 666…= (　　　　)　　(2) 5.608 608…= (　　　　)

(3) 4.109 209 20…= (　　　　)

14 $2 \div 11 =$ (   ). (Express the quotient with a recurring decimal)

15 A recurring decimal greater than $4.\dot{6}$ but less than $4.\dot{7}$ is (   ).

16 If the decimal point of a number is moved two places to the right, the resulting number is increased by (   ) times the original number.

17 When the quotient of $13.2 \div 0.45$ is 29, the remainder is (   ).

18 When a decimal number with two decimal places is rounded off to the nearest tenth, it is 7.0. The greatest value of the decimal number could be (   ), and its least value could be (   ).

(B) **Multiple choice questions.** (5 marks in total)

19 In the four numbers 0.808, $0.\dot{8}0\dot{8}$, $0.80\dot{8}$ and $0.80\dot{8}$, the least number is (   ).

(A) 0.808 (B) $0.\dot{8}0\dot{8}$ (C) $0.8\dot{0}\dot{8}$ (D) $0.80\dot{8}$

20 Rounding $0.\dot{9}\dot{8}$ to the nearest hundredth, it is (   ).

(A) 0.99   (B) 1.00   (C) 9.00   (D) 1

21 If $a \div 0.09 = b \div 0.1$ (both a and b are greater than 0), then a (   ) b.

(A) $>$ (B) $<$ (C) $=$ (D) uncertain

22 When the quotient of $78.35 \div 2.6$ is rounded to the nearest tenth, it is (   ).

(A) 30   (B) 30.2   (C) 30.13   (D) 30.1

23 When a decimal number with two decimal places is rounded off, the result is 6.8. The range of possible values that the number can take is (   ).

(A) greater than or equal to 6.75 but less than 6.85

(B) greater than or equal to 6.74 but less than 6.84

(C) greater than or equal to 6.70 but less than 6.85

(D) greater than or equal to 6.75 but less than 6.84

Chapter 3 Statistics

3.1 Mean

Basic questions

1. Fill in the brackets.
   (1) Mean=(   )÷(   ).
   (2) There are five packs of sugar with a total weight of 560 grams. The mean weight per pack of sugar is (   ) grams.
   (3) A farm raises 150 pigs weighing 9 tonnes in total. The mean weight of each pig is (   ) kilograms.
   (4) In mid-term tests, Xiao Qiao scored 99 marks in mathematics, 96 marks in English and 90 marks in Chinese. The mean score per subject was (   ) marks.

2. Find the mean of the numbers in each group.
   (1) 56, 90, 108, 312.

   (2) 72 kilograms, 94 kilograms, 159 kilograms, 511 kilograms, 788 kilograms.

3. The table below shows the amount of money that Teacher Zhang paid for electricity in the four quarters of a year.

Quarter	First	Second	Third	Fourth
Electricity bill (yuan)	566	308	1027	429

   (1) How much did Teacher Zhang pay for electricity in the whole year?

(2) How much was the payment for the electricity bill per quarter on average?

4 The statistical table below shows the information about pupils in Class 5(1) joining extra-curricular clubs in a school.

Club	Football	Basketball	Table tennis	Computer	Photography
No. of pupils	8	6	10	12	4

Question: How many pupils are there in each club on average?

5 The heights and weights of 6 pupils in one group of a class in Guangming Primary School are shown in the table below.

Pupil number	One	Two	Three	Four	Five	Six
Height (cm)	138	152	140	145	155	143
Weight (kg)	33	41	38	44	43	35

Question: (1) How many centimetres is the mean height of these six pupils?

(2) How many kilograms is their mean weight?

6 Xiao Dingding scored the following marks in the six mathematics tests this semester: 98, 94, 92, 95, 100 and 97. Question: How many marks was the mean score of the six tests?

Enhancement and extension

7 There are 15 winners in a mathematics competition and the marks they scored are 98, 90, 88, 84, 90, 92, 95, 89, 94, 91, 90, 92, 88, 81 and 91. Question: How many marks is the mean score of these pupils?

3.2 Calculation of the mean (1)

Basic questions

1 Fill in the brackets.

(1) Four identical glasses are filled with water. The heights of the water levels are 3.2 centimetres, 4.5 centimetres, 5.5 centimetres and 6.4 centimetres. The mean height of the water levels in the four glasses is (   ) centimetres.

(2) A children's palace choir has 5 groups. The numbers of members in these groups are 37, 40, 39, 36 and 32. The number of members in each group on average is (   ).

2 Multiple choice questions.

(1) There are 6 boxes of table tennis balls in a school activity room. The numbers of the tennis balls in these boxes are 4, 6, 6, 6, 7 and 7. How many table tennis balls are there in each box on average? Of the following statements, the correct one(s) is/are (   ).

(A) $(4+6+6+6+7+7)\div 6$ (B) $(4+6\times 3+7\times 2)\div 3$

(C) $(4+6+7)\div 3$ (D) $(4+6\times 3+7\times 2)\div 6$

(2) Two classes of Grade 5 pupils made paper flowers for the children in a kindergarten. Class 1 made a total of 120 paper flowers in 2 hours. Class 2 spent 3 hours, making 70 paper flowers per hour on average. How many paper flowers did each of the two classes make per hour on average? Of the following statements, the correct one(s) is/are (   ).

(A) $(120+70)\div 2$ (B) $(120+70\times 3)\div(2+3)$

(C) $(120+70\times 3)\div 2$ (D) $(120\times 2+70\times 3)\div(2+3)$

3 Xiao Ling did mathematics enrichment questions every day from Monday to Friday. The table below shows the statistics.

Day	Monday	Tuesday	Wednesday	Thursday	Friday
No. of questions	10	8	10	7	12

Question: How many questions did Xiao Ling do per day on average?

4 A rice mill milled 20 tonnes of rice in the morning and 26 tonnes of rice in the afternoon on the first day. On the second day, it milled 47 tonnes of rice, and on the third day, it milled 39 tonnes of rice. How many tonnes of rice did it mill per day on average in the three days?

5 It took Xiao Qiao 7 days to finish reading a comic book. The numbers of pages that she read each day were: 24, 22, 24, 24, 21, 22 and 24. How many pages did she read every day on average?

6 A vehicle travelled from place A to place B. It travelled 160 kilometres in the first 2 hours and 210 kilometres in the next 3 hours. How many kilometres did the vehicle travel per hour on average?

7 A fruit store received a batch of fruit. It sold 150 kilograms in the first 3 days, 160 kilograms in the next 5 days, and 350 kilograms in the last 7 days. How many kilograms of the fruit were sold per day on average?

8 A delivery team delivered rice to a supermarket. On the first day, the team made 7 trips and delivered 1550 kilograms of rice. On the second day, it made 8 trips and delivered 1750 kilograms of rice. How many kilograms of rice did the team deliver per day on average in the two days? How many kilograms of rice did the team deliver per trip on average?

9 There are 20 boys and 16 girls in Class 5(1). In an English test, the boys' mean score is 88.8 marks and the girls' is 91.5 marks. Question: What is the mean score of the whole class in the English test?

Enhancement and extension

10 There are 7 numbers with a mean of 62. If 2 of the numbers with a mean of 56 were removed, then what is the mean of the remaining numbers?

3.3 Calculation of the mean (2)

Basic questions

1 Multiple choice questions.

(1) Xiao Pang does exercises. The distances he ran in 5 days are recorded below: 650 metres, 880 metres, 1050 metres, 0 metres and 930 metres. How many metres did he run each day on average? The correct calculation of the following is (　　).

(A) $(650 + 880 + 1050 + 930) \div 4$
$= 3510 \div 4$
$= 877.5$ (metres)

(B) $(650 + 880 + 1050 + 0 + 930) \div 5$
$= 3510 \div 5$
$= 702$ (metres)

(2) Two classes of Grade 5 pupils made paper flowers for the children in a kindergarten. Class 1 spent 2 hours, making 60 paper flowers per hour on average. Class 2 spent 3 hours, making 70 paper flowers per hour on average. How many paper flowers did each class make on average? The correct expression of the following is (　　).

(A) $(60 + 70) \div 2$　　(B) $(60 + 70) \div (2 + 3)$
(C) $(60 \times 2 + 70 \times 3) \div 2$　　(D) $(60 \times 2 + 70 \times 3) \div (2 + 3)$

2 The table below shows the statistics of milk Xiao Lin drank in a week.

Day	Monday	Tuesday	Wednesday	Thursday	Friday	Saturday	Sunday
Amount of milk drunk (mL)	150	200	0	180	0	220	160

Question: How many millilitres of milk did Xiao Lin drink per day on average in the week?

3 The numbers of toys made by a toy factory in a week (5 days) were: 732, 698, 628, 0 and 1254. How many toys were made per day on average in the 5 days?

4 The information about Xiao Pang's participation in community activities in the first half of a year is shown below.

Month	January	February	March	April	May	June
No. of times	2	3	2	0	2	1

Question: How many times did Xiao Pang take part in community activities per month on average? (Keep your answer to one decimal place)

5 A vehicle travelled from place A to place B. It travelled 65 kilometres per hour on average in the first 2 hours and 75 kilometres per hour on average in the next 3 hours. How many kilometres did the vehicle travel per hour on average?

6 The table below shows the number of skips that Xiao Pang did in rope skipping practices.

Time	1st	2nd	3rd	4th	5th	6th	7th	8th	9th	10th
No. of skips	35	35	35	48	50	35	50	34	48	50

Question: How many skips did he do each time on average?

7 The table below shows the numbers of boys and girls as well as their mean weights in Classes 5(1) and (2). Using the data in the table, calculate the following.

Staistical table on the weights of boys and girls in Class 5(1) and Class 5(2)

Class	Gender	No. of pupils	Mean weight (kilograms)
Class 5(1)	Boys	16	41.5
	Girls	14	38.5
Class 5(2)	Boys	15	41.8
	Girls	15	37.2

(1) What is the mean weight of the pupils in Class 5(1)?

(2) What is the mean weight of the pupils in Class 5(2)?

(3) What is the mean weight of all the boys in the two classes? (Round to the nearest tenth)

(4) What is the mean weight of all the girls in the two classes? (Round to the nearest tenth)

Enhancement and extension

8 There are three numbers: Number A, Number B and Number C. The mean of Number A and Number B is 36, the mean of Number B and Number C is 30, and the mean of Number A and Number C is 39. What is the mean of these three numbers?

3.4 Application of the mean (1)

Basic questions

1. Fill in the brackets.

(1) Xiao Qiao completed 54 mental sums in 1.5 minutes, and Xiao Pang completed 76 mental sums in 2 minutes. Xiao Qiao did (　　　) mental sums per minute and Xiao Pang did (　　　) mental sums per minute. (　　　) did it faster.

(2) Two teams had a competition in making paper flowers. There are 9 members in the first team and 8 members in the second team. The first team made 108 paper flowers and the second team made 100 during the same period of time. The members in the (　　　) team made paper flowers faster.

2. The statistical table below shows the results of 1-minute rope skipping competition between Group 1 and Group 2.

Results of 1-minute rope skipping: Group 1

Name	Zhang Ming	Li Hong	Wang Gang	Yang Bo	Lin Hai
No. of skips	56	44	60	58	47

Results of 1-minute rope skipping: Group 2

Name	Xiao Dingding	Xiao Pang	Xiao Ya	Xiao Qiao
No. of skips	50	47	59	62

(1) On average, how many skips did each member in Group 1 do in one minute?

(2) On average, how many skips did each member in Group 2 do in one minute?

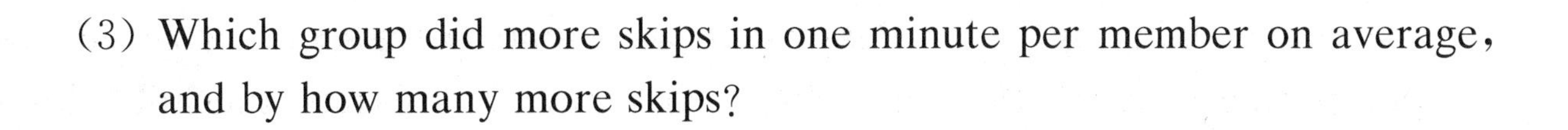

(3) Which group did more skips in one minute per member on average, and by how many more skips?

3 Car A travelled 238 kilometres in 3.5 hours and Car B travelled 260 kilometres in 4 hours. Question: Which car travelled at a faster speed?

4 There are 5 people in Xiao Dingding's family and they drink 6 litres of water in 1 day. There are 4 people in Xiao Pang's family and they drink 5 litres of water in 1 day. There are 3 people in Xiao Qiao's family and they drink 4 litres of water in 1 day. Which family drinks the most amount of water per person per day?

5 A factory's assembly workshop has three teams. Team 1 has 12 workers and can assemble 162 spare parts in a day. Team 2 has 15 workers and can assemble 195 spare parts in a day. Team 3 has 16 workers and can assemble 224 spare parts in a day. Which team is the fastest in assembling the spare parts?

6 Xiao Pang and his parents went hill hiking during a two-day weekend. On the way walking up, Xiao Pang spent 48 minutes at a speed of 36 metres per minute to reach the peak. When he came down from the hill taking the same path, it only took him 32 minutes.

(a) What was Xiao Pang's average speed per minute when he came down the hill?

(b) What was his average speed per minute in the entire journey of walking up and walking down?

Enhancement and extension

7 A sales assistant in a shop mixed 2 kilograms of milk sweets, 3 kilograms of cola-flavoured sweets and 5 kilograms of chocolates together. If the milk sweets are 12.8 yuan per kilogram, the cola-flavoured sweets are 8.8 yuan per kilogram and the chocolates are 9.8 yuan per kilogram, then what is the price of the assorted sweets per kilogram?

3.5 Application of the mean (2)

Basic questions

1 Fill in the brackets.

(1) Xiao Pang walked 15 metres in 25 steps. His average step was (   ) metres.

(2) Xiao Ya can walk 56 steps in one minute on average. If each step is 0.5 metres, then Xiao Ya can walk (   ) metres in one minute.

(3) Xiao Dingding walked five times from a school gate to his classroom to estimate the distance. The number of steps he walked each time was respectively 62, 59, 61, 61 and 60. From the school gate to the classroom, Xiao Dingding needs to walk about (   ) steps.

(4) Person A walked 20 steps and Person B walked 25 steps to cover the same distance of 10 metres. The average length of steps of Person A is (   ) centimetres more than that of Person B.

2 Xiao Qiao wanted to know the distance she could walk in one minute. She tested it 6 times and the distances recorded were 59 steps, 63 steps, 65 steps, 60 steps, 61 steps and 64 steps.

(1) How many steps did Xiao Qiao walk in one minute on average?

(2) If the average length of her step is 45 centimetres, then how many metres could she walk in 1 minute?

(3) It takes Xiao Qiao 20 minutes to walk from home to her school. Please find out about how many metres the distance is between her home and the school.

(4) The distance between Xiao Qiao's home and Xiao Dingding's home is about 446.4 metres. About how many minutes will it take Xiao Qiao to walk from her home to Xiao Dingding's home?

❸ The table below shows the information about after-school reading Wang Qiang did in a week.

Day	Monday	Tuesday	Wednesday	Thursday	Friday	Saturday	Sunday
Amount of reading (words)	1800	2000	2100	2400	1600	1500	2600

(1) How many words did Wang Qiang read per day on average?

(2) About how many days will it take Wang Qiang to finish reading a book of 48 000 words?

(3) Based on the same efficiency, about how many thousand words can Wang Qiang read in a year (365 days)?

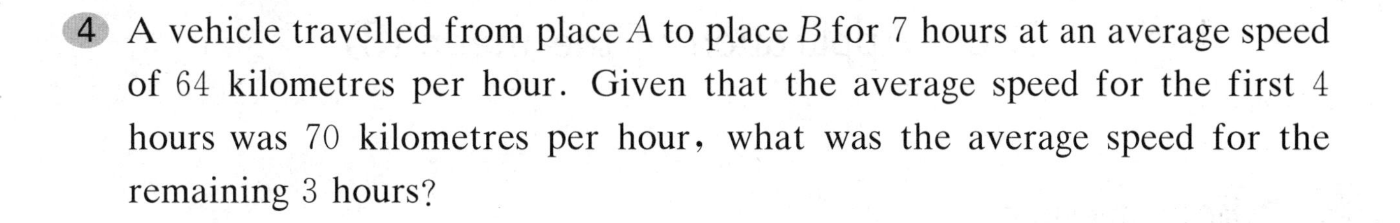

4 A vehicle travelled from place A to place B for 7 hours at an average speed of 64 kilometres per hour. Given that the average speed for the first 4 hours was 70 kilometres per hour, what was the average speed for the remaining 3 hours?

5 There are three numbers A, B and C. The mean of Number A and Number B is 84. The mean of Number B and Number C is 92. Number B is 85. Find the mean of these three numbers.

Enhancement and extension

6 In a mathematics test, the mean score of a class was 91.2 marks, but Liu Huan was absent due to illness. After Liu Huan had a make-up test and scored 98 marks, the mean score of the whole class was brought up to 91.4 marks. How many pupils are there in the class in total?

3.6 Application of the mean (3)

Basic questions

1 Fill in the brackets.

(1) Number A is 36, Number B is 42, Number C is 54, and Number D is 72. The mean of the four numbers is (　　　　).

(2) The mean of Number A and Number B is 39. The mean of Number C and Number D is 63. The mean of the four numbers is (　　　　).

(3) The mean of Number A, Number B and Number C is 44. Number D is 72. The mean of the four numbers is (　　　　).

(4) The mean of Number A, Number B, Number C and Number D is 51. The mean of Number A, Number B and Number C is 44. The mean of Number C and Number D is 63. Number C is (　　　　).

2 There are five boxes of biscuits weighing 240 grams, 300 grams, 360 grams, 380 grams and 420 grams.

(1) What is the weight of each box on average?

(2) After one box of biscuits was eaten, the mean weight of the remaining biscuits per box is 330 grams. What is the weight of the box of biscuits that was eaten?

3 In a mathematics test, the mean score of Xiao Dingding, Xiao Pang and Xiao Qiao was 92 marks, and the mean score of Xiao Ya and Xiao Ming was 95 marks.

(1) What is the mean score of the five pupils?

(2) If Xiao Ming scored 4 more marks than Xiao Ya, and Xiao Ya scored 2 more marks than Xiao Pang, and Xiao Pang scored 1 more mark than Xiao Qiao, then how many marks did Xiao Dingding score?

4. In a rope skipping competition, Xiao Hua did 135 skips, 146 skips and 150 skips, respectively, for the first three attempts. To achieve an average of 148 skips, how many skips must Xiao Hua do in the fourth attempt?

5. The mean score of a class of 40 pupils was 92.5 marks in an end-of-year mathematics test, with two pupils absent due to illness. In their make-up test, they scored 95 and 100 marks. What was the new mean score of the class?

6. The distance between place A and place B is 3600 kilometres. It takes an airplane 4.5 hours to fly from place A to place B, and 5.1 hours to return from place B to place A. How many kilometres does the airplane fly for a round trip between the two places in one hour on average?

7 After a mid-term test, Xiao Qiao calculated the mean score of the whole class for the mathematics test, which was 88.4 marks. Later when reviewing her calculation, she found a mistake. She mistook one pupil's score of 89.5 as 80.5. After recalculation, the mean score was 88.7 marks. How many pupils were there in the class?

Enhancement and extension

8 Mr Li made 128 spare parts on the first day, 156 spare parts on the second day and 164 spare parts on the third day. The number of spare parts he made on the fourth day was 14 more than the mean number of the spare parts he made in these four days. How many spare parts did Mr Li make in the four days in total?

Unit test 3

A. Fill in the brackets. (30 marks in total)

1. In three mathematics tests, Xiao Qin scored 94 marks, 92 marks and 99 marks. The mean score of these three mathemtics tests was (　　　) marks.

2. The heights of six pupils are 150 cm, 143 cm, 149 cm, 155 cm, 161 cm and 157 cm. Their average height is between (　　　) cm and (　　　) cm.

3. Number A is 30, which is 6 less than Number B and twice Number C. The mean of Number A, Number B and Number C is (　　　).

4. The mean of three numbers is 15.6. If 13.2 is included as a fourth number, then the mean of the four numbers is (　　　).

5. The mean of Number A, Number B and Number C is 48. The mean of Number A and Number B is 49. Number C is (　　　).

6. A fruit store delivered fruit to a kindergarten. 15 kilograms was delivered the first time. The amount delivered the second time was 1.2 times the amount delivered the first time. The fruit was equally shared by 6 classes. Each class received (　　　) kilograms.

7. The mean of five numbers is 60. Going from the least to the greatest, the first three numbers have a mean of 44. Going from the greatest to the least, the first three numbers have a mean of 72. The number in the middle place is (　　　).

8. Xiao Wang walked five steps and measured the lengths. The results were 46 cm, 48 cm, 48 cm, 50 cm and 52 cm. The mean length of Xiao Wang's steps was about (　　　) cm.

9 The mean of Number A, Number B and Number C is 28. The sum of Number D and Number E is 64. The mean of these five numbers is (   ).

10 The mean score of three pupils A, B and C in a Chinese test is 85 marks. The fourth pupil D must score (   ) marks so that the mean score of the four pupils is 87 marks.

11 A staff member in a supermarket made a careless mistake. He misread the weight of one of the five bags of rice as 30 kilograms. Therefore, he obtained the mean weight of each bag as 60 kilograms, while the actual mean weight should be 70 kilograms. The weight of the misread bag of rice was (   ) kilograms.

12 Red Star electrical appliance store sold 105 colour TVs in 7 days in the first week and 147 sets in 7 days in the second week. On average, it sold (   ) colour TVs per week and (   ) TVs per day in the two weeks.

13 It took a messenger 5.5 hours to travel from place A to place B at a speed of 18 kilometres per hour. On the return journey from place B to place A, he travelled at 22 kilometres per hour. The average speed of the messenger travelled for the whole journey was (   ) kilometres per hour.

14 Xiao Lin took three mathematics tests. She scored 90 marks in the first test and 98 marks in the second. Her score in the third test was 2 marks higher than the mean score of the three tests. Xiao Lin scored (   ) marks in the third test.

15 Each of the following three ○s stands for a digit, and it is used to form a one-digit number, a two-digit number and a three-digit number: ○, ○8 and ○69, respectively. The mean of the three numbers is 152. The sum of the three digits that the ○s stand for is (   ).

B. Multiple choice questions. (10 marks in total)

16 One clothing store sold 360 sets of clothes on the first day and 450 sets on the second day. On the third day, it sold 160 sets in the morning and 180 sets in the afternoon. How many sets of clothes did it sell each day on average? The correct expression of the following is (　　).

(A) $(360+450+160+180)\div 2$　　(B) $(360+450+160+180)\div 3$

(C) $(360+450+160+180)\div 4$　　(D) $(360+450+160+180)\div 6$

17 Xiao Pang practised shuttlecock kicking in a week. The number of kicks he practised for each day was respectively 200, 160, 190, 160, 190, 160 and 200. How many kicks did he practise per day on average in the week? The correct expression of the following is (　　).

(A) $(200+160+190)\div 3$

(B) $(200\times 3+160\times 2+190\times 2)\div 7$

(C) $(200\times 2+160\times 2+190\times 3)\div 7$

(D) $(200\times 2+160\times 3+190\times 2)\div 7$

18 Class 5(1) had a mathematics test. The mean scores of different groups were as follows: the mean score of Group One and Group Two was 92 marks, the mean score of Group Two and Group Three was 91 marks, and the mean score of Group Three and Group Four was 91.5 marks. The correct expression of the mean score of all the groups in the whole class was (　　).

(A) $(92+91+91.5)\div 3$　　(B) $(92+91)\times 2\div 4$

(C) $(91+91.5)\times 2\div 4$　　(D) $(92+91.5)\times 2\div 4$

19 The number of boys in a class is half the number of the girls. The mean height of the boys is 154 centimetres and the mean height of the girls is 148 centimetres. The mean height of the whole class is (　　) centimetres.

(A) 149　　(B) 150　　(C) 152　　(D) uncertain

20 Three vehicles delivered a total of 68 tonnes of rice in six trips and another five vehicles delivered a total of 84 tonnes of rice in 4 trips. How many tonnes of rice did each vehicle deliver in each trip on average? The correct

expression of the following is (　　).

(A) $(68+84)\div 2$

(B) $(68\div 3\div 6+92\div 5\div 4)\div 2$

(C) $(68+84)\div(3\times 6+5\times 4)$

(D) $(68+84)\div(3+5)\div(6+4)$

C. Application problems. (60 marks in total)

21 A mechanical maintenance studio has three workshops. There are 147 workers in the first workshop. The second and the third workshops have the same number of workers, each with 153 people. How many workers are there in each workshop on average?

22 There are two classrooms. There are 120 pupils in Classroom A with an area of 50 square metres. There are 150 pupils in Classroom B with an area of 60 square metres. Which classroom is more crowded?

23 The table below shows the amount of time Xiao Qiao spent helping her mum with housework in a week. Answer the questions according to the statistical table.

Day	Monday	Tuesday	Wednesday	Thursday	Friday	Saturday	Sunday
Time (minutes)	30	28	15	0	23	40	32

(1) How many minutes did Xiao Qiao spend helping her mum with housework each day on average in the week?

(2) Following the above calculation, how much time would Xiao Qiao spend helping her mum with housework in a month (30 days)?

24 The amount of grass a cow ate from January to June is shown in the table below.

Month	January	February	March	April	May	June
Amount of grass eaten (kilograms)	300	350	330	350	350	300

(1) On average, how many kilograms of grass did the cow eat each month from January to June?

(2) About how many kilograms of grass would the cow eat in a year?

25 Xiao Dingding walked 10 steps four times and measured the distances covered. The results were 4.2 metres, 4.8 metres, 4.6 metres and 4.8 metres.

(1) What was the average length of a single step of Xiao Dingding?

(2) Xiao Dingding walked 5 times from his home to a gate of the residential area. It took him 120 steps, 136 steps, 128 steps, 130 steps and 126 steps. About how many metres is the distance from Xiao Dingding's home to the gate of the residential area?

(3) Xiao Dingding walked 8500 steps from his home to the entrance of a supermarket. How many kilometres away is his home from the supermarket?

26 A road maintenance team was repairing a road. It repaired 36 metres per day on average in the first 12 days and 630 metres in total in the next 18 days. How many metres of the road were repaired per day on average?

27 A toy factory made 2400 toy dolls in January, which was 200 dolls more than in February. The number of dolls made in March was the same as in January. The number of dolls made in April was 600 more than in February. How many dolls did the factory make per month on average in these four months?

28 The table below shows the mean scores of three classes in Grade 5 in an English test and the numbers of pupils in these classes.

Class	Class 1	Class 2	Class 3
No. of pupils	32	28	30
Mean score (marks)	90	91.5	88

(1) Please calculate the total score of each of these three classes.

(2) What is the mean score of the three classes on average?

(3) What is the mean score of all the pupils in the three classes?

29 Class 5(1) and Class 5(2) had a basketball shooting competition. The table below shows the information.

Class 5(1)	Member no.	One	Two	Three	Four	Five	Six	Seven	Eight	Nine	Ten
	No. of goals	12	8	10	9	11	9	8	6	15	16
Class 5(2)	Member no.	One	Two	Three	Four	Five	Six	Seven	Eight	Nine	
	No. of goals	8	9	12	11	5	10	12	9	14	

(1) How many goals did each member make on average in Class 5(1) and Class 5(2), respectively?

(b) How many goals did each member make on average in the two classes altogether? (Give your answer to one decimal place)

30 Two groups of workers are to process spare parts of the same type. On average, each worker is to process 120 spare parts. Given that there are 15 workers in Group One, each worker in Group One is to process 128 spare parts on average, and each worker in Group Two is to process 115 spare parts on average, how many workers are there in Group Two?

Chapter 4 Simple equations

4.1 Using letters to represent numbers (1)

Basic questions

1 What number does each of the following letters represent?

(1) 3, 6, 9, A, 15　　$A=$ ______

(2) 2, 1, 2, 3, 2, 4, 5, 6, B, 7, 8, 9　　$B=$ ______

(3) $2+6=3+M$　　$M=$ ______

(4) $15\div 3=10-Y$　　$Y=$ ______

(5) 1, 4, 9, 16, 25, 36, 49, C, 81　　$C=$ ______

(6) 1, 5, 2, 10, 3, 15, X, 20, 5, Y, 6　　$X=$ ______, $Y=$ ______

2 Fill in the brackets.

(1) $m\times 8$ can be simply written as (　　　　).

(2) $x\times 3\times y$ can be simply written as (　　　　).

(3) $(9+a)\times 6$ can be simply written as (　　　　).

(4) $n\times 1+a\div 2$ can be simply written as (　　　　).

(5) $a\times a$ can be simply written as (　　　　).

(6) $b+b+b$ can be simply written as (　　　　).

3 What laws of operations or properties of operations are used in the following expressions?

(1) $(a+b)+c=a+(b+c)$　(　　　　).

(2) $a(b+c)=ab+ac$　(　　　　).

(3) $a\div b=(a\div c)\div(b\div c)$ $(b\neq 0, c\neq 0)$　(　　　　).

(4) $a-b-c=a-(b+c)$　(　　　　).

4 Use expressions with letters to express the relations between the quantities in the following questions.

(1) In a triangle, if $\angle 1=a^\circ$ and $\angle 2=b^\circ$, then $\angle 3=$ (　　　　).

(2) In an isosceles triangle, if the base angle is a°, the degree of the vertex angle is (　　　　).

(3) If the perimeter of a square is C, then the side length of the square is ( ).

(4) If A represents the unit price, X represents the quantity and C represents the total price, then $X=$( ).

(5) Given a rectangle, if its area is S and the length is a, then the width is ( ).

(6) One frog has 1 mouth, 2 eyes and 4 legs. Two frogs have 2 mouths, 4 eyes and 8 legs. Three frogs have ( ) mouths, ( ) eyes and ( ) legs. x frogs have ( ) mouths, ( ) eyes and ( ) legs.

5 Fill in the table. Use expressions with letters to express the relations between three quantities.

Speed (metres/minute)	Time	Distance
65	t	
v		210
	6	s

Number of sets made per day	Number of working days	Total number of sets made
x		480
	25	x
30	x	

Unit price	Quantity	Total price
8.5	b	
	y	x
a		z

Enhancement and extension

6. If the sum of three consecutive even numbers is a, then the number in the middle is (　　　　), the least number is (　　　　) and the greatest number is (　　　　).

7. In the following column calculations, each of the four letters represents a one place digit. What digits do A, B, C and D represent respectively to make the column expressions true?

$$\begin{array}{r} A\ B \\ +\ C\ D \\ \hline 9\ 4 \end{array} \qquad \begin{array}{r} A\ B \\ -\ C\ D \\ \hline 5\ 8 \end{array}$$

$A=$ (　　)　　$B=$ (　　)　　$C=$ (　　)　　$D=$ (　　)

4.2 Using letters to represent numbers (2)

Basic questions

1 Multiple choice questions.

(1) a^2 is equal to (　　).

(A) $a \times 2$　　(B) $a+2$　　(C) $a \times a$

(2) Comparing $2x$ and x^2, the result is (　　)

(A) $2x > x^2$　　(B) $2x = x^2$　　(C) $2x < x^2$　　(D) uncertain

(3) Dingding is younger than Xinxin. This year Dingding is a years old and Xinxin is b years old. After two years, Dingding is (　　) years younger than Xinxin.

(A) 2　　(B) $b-a$　　(C) $a-b$　　(D) $b-a+2$

(4) Number A is a, which is b less than 4 times Number B. Number B is (　　).

(A) $a \div 4 - b$　　(B) $(a-b) \div 4$　　(C) $(a+b) \div 4$

2 Use expressions with letters to represent the relations between quantities below.

(1) 100 minus the sum of a and b.

____

(2) The quotient of 5 divided by x plus n.

____

(3) The result of subtracting 2 from 6 times s.

____

(4) Subtracting m times 12 from 320.

____

(5) The sum of 80 and b multiplied by 5.

____

(6) 6 times the sum of b and 90.

____

3 Write the expressions based on the given conditions below.

A toy robot costs 50 yuan, a toy airplane costs m yuan, and a toy car costs n yuan.

(1) To buy a toy robot and a toy car costs (　　　　) yuan in total.

(2) To buy a toy airplane and two toy cars costs (　　　　) yuan in total.

(3) To buy a toy robot, a toy airplane and a toy car costs (　　　　) yuan

in total.

(4) To buy two toy airplanes and 3 toy cars costs ( ) yuan in total.

(5) A toy airplane costs ( ) yuan more than a toy car.

4 Use expressions with letters to express the quantities below.

(1) A car has travelled t hours at a speed of 85 kilometres per hour. It has travelled ( ) kilometres in total.

(2) Xiao Pang spent 6 days reading m pages of a book. He read ( ) pages of the book each day on average.

(3) There are 24 basketballs and n footballs. There are ( ) fewer footballs than basketballs.

(4) A shirt costs a yuan, and a pair of trousers costs b yuan. The total cost for buying 3 sets of these clothes is ( ) yuan.

5 Short answer questions.

(1) On 1st May, a particular model of mobile phone was selling well in a Suning store. It sold 75 sets in the morning and 100 sets in the afternoon. Given that each set costs a yuan, what was the total value of the sales for the whole day? How much less was the sales value in the morning than in the afternoon?

(2) An x-metre-long highway was to be built. The plan was to build m metres each day. In practice, 2.5 metres more than planned was completed each day. In how many days was the task actually completed?

Enhancement and extension

6 As shown in the diagram, there are some circles with the equal radius inside each of the identical squares. Please observe carefully and then fill in the table.

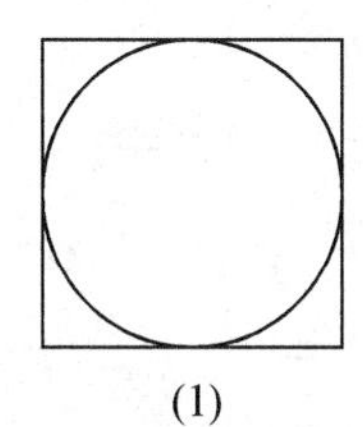

(1)

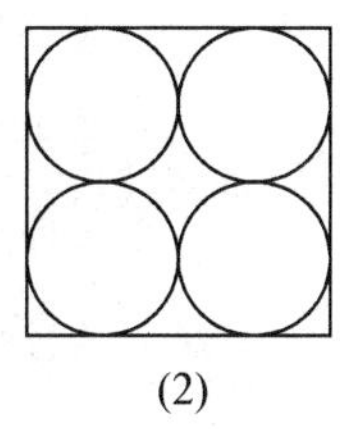

(2)

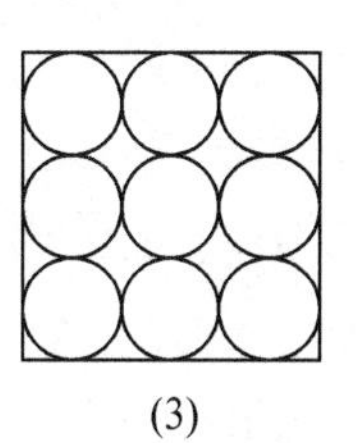

(3)

......

Figure no.	(1)	(2)	(3)	(4)	(5)	(6)	......
No. of cicles							

The number of cirlces in the nth square is (   ).
Based on the pattern you identified, there are (   ) circles in the 2008th figure.

4.3 Simplification and evaluation (1)

Basic questions

1 Simplify the following expressions.

(1) $5x + 4x =$

(2) $5b + 4b - 9a =$

(3) $7x + 7 + 6x =$

(4) $5b + 4b - 9b =$

(5) $36s - 15t - 24s + 35t =$

(6) $48x + 75y - 18x - 6x =$

(7) $5 \times 12a =$

(8) $36k \div 9 =$

(9) $6 \times 3x \div 2 =$

(10) $4y \div 2 \times 10 =$

(11) $75x \div 15 + 6 \times 9x =$

(12) $4n \times 7 - 63n \div 9 - 3n =$

2 True or false. (Put a "√" for true and a "×" for false.)

(1) $6 + a = 6a$ ( )

(2) $n + n - m + m = 2n - 2m$ ( )

(3) $5x + 4 + x = 10x$ ( )

3 Fill in the brackets.

(1) In an equilateral triangle, the length of each side is a metres. Its perimeter is ( ) metres.

(2) Xiao Hua has x pencils. Xiao Qiang has 3 more pencils than Xiao Hua. They have ( ) pencils altogether.

(3) Each bag of flour weighs 10 kilograms. Each bag of rice weighs x kilograms. y bags of flour and 5 bags of rice weigh ( ) kilograms in total.

(4) A school bought x boxes of red chalk sticks. The number of boxes of white chalk sticks it bought was 10 times as many as red chalk sticks. The school bought ( ) boxes of chalk sticks altogether.

(5) Each pen costs a yuan, Xiao Ya, Xiao Pang and Xiao Qiao each bought 4 pens and they needed to pay ( ) yuan in total; each copy of an exercise book costs 2 yuan, Xiao Ya, Xiao Pang and Xiao Qiao each bought b copies and they needed to pay ( ) yuan in total.

4 Short answer questions.

(1) 10 yuan can buy $3a$ kilograms of a fruit. Based on this price, how many kilograms of the fruit can Huanhuan buy with 50 yuan?

(2) It took Xiao Qiao m hours to make 21 paper flowers. It took Xiao Ya 2 hours to make n paper flowers. How many paper flowers did each of them make on average? How many paper flowers did each of them make each hour on average?

(3) The dividend is 6 times the divisor. If the divisor is x, then what is the sum of the dividend, divisor and quotient?

Enhancement and extension

5 Three small rectangles, each with length 5 centimetres and width a centimetres, form a large rectangle. What is the area of the large rectangle? What is the perimeter?

6 The length and width of a rectangle are a centimetres and b centimetres, respectively, and $a > b$. The side length of a square is equal to the difference between the two sides of the rectangle. How many centimetres is the sum of their perimeters?

4.4 Simplification and evaluation (2)

Basic questions

1. Fill in the table with numbers.

A book costs 7 yuan. To buy a number of books, the relation between the total price and the number of books can be expressed as $7a = b$. When $a = 1, 3, 5, 7, 9, \cdots$, what value does b represent, respectively?

a	1	3	5	7	9
b					

2. A section of a road is to be repaired. c metres of the road was repaired each day on average for the first 6 days, and there were s metres left.

(1) Use an expression to express the length of this section of the road: (　　　　)

(2) When $c = 50$ and $s = 200$, the length of the road is (　　　　).

3. The side length of a square is a centimetres. Its perimeter is (　　　　) centimetres, and its area is (　　　　) square centimetres. When $a = 5$ centimetres, the perimeter is (　　　　) centimetres and the area is (　　　　) square centimetres.

4. Simplify first and then evaluate.

(1) When $x = 2.5$, find the value of $18x - 8x$.

(2) When $y = 2$, find the value of $12y \div 6 \times 5$.

(3) When $m = 4$ and $n = 1.8$, find the value of $15m + 5m - 18n - 12n$.

(4) When $a = 0.5$ and $b = 0.6$, find the value of $3.5a \times 8 + 75b \div 15$.

5 Solve each of the following questions as required.

(1) Qingqing Forest Farm has cultivated sycamores and cedars, each in x rows. The number of sycamores cultivated in each row is 12, while the number of cedars in each row is 14.

① How many sycamores and cedars has the farm cultivated in total?

② When $x = 20$, how many sycamores and cedars are there in total in the Qingqing Forest Farm?

(2) A vehicle travelled at a speed of a kilometres per hour. It travelled 4 hours in the morning and b kilometres in the afternoon.

① Use an expression with letters to express the distance that the vehicle travelled.

② When $a = 80$ and $b = 200$, what is the distance the vehicle travelled?

(3) In Yangguang Primary School, a pupils joined the track and field team. The number of pupils joined the choir team was 4 less than twice the number of pupils joining the track and field team.

① Use an expression with letters to express the total number of pupils in the two teams.

② When $a = 24$, how many pupils are there in the two teams?

Enhancement and extension

6 To buy 1 kilogram of bananas and 3 kilograms of apples, it costs m yuan. To buy 2 kilograms of bananas and 5 kilograms of apples, it costs n yuan. How much does 1 kilogram of apples cost? When $m = 54$ and $n = 93$, how much does 1 kilogram of apples cost?

4.5 Equations (1)

Basic questions

1 True or false. (Put a "√" for true and a "×" for false)

(1) An expression with one(or more) variable(s) is called an equation. (   )

(2) $7x - 6x$ is an equation. (   )

(3) $9 - 3x$ does not have an "=" sign, therefore it is not an equation. (   )

(4) $4x - 20 = y$ is not an equation. (   )

(5) $6x \div 2 = 2x + 8$ is an equation. (   )

2 Multiple choice questions.

(1) In the following, (   ) is not an equation.

(A) $18x + 5x = 23x$ (B) $5(a + b) = 5a + 5b$

(C) $6x - x - 2x$ (D) $6y - 8 = 40$

(2) In the following, (   ) is an equation with one variable.

(A) $C = 2(a + b)$ (B) $18 - 2m < 5$

(C) $9 \times 0.9 = 8.1$ (D) $x \div 6 = 0$

(3) Given: $\triangle + \triangle + \bigcirc = 19$ and $\triangle + \bigcirc = 12$, then: $\triangle =$ (   ) and $\bigcirc =$ (   ).

(A) 9 3 (B) 8 4 (C) 7 5 (D) 5 7

(4) Given: $\bigcirc = \triangle + \triangle + \triangle$ and $\bigcirc \times \triangle = 108$, then: $\bigcirc + \triangle =$ (   ).

(A) 18 (B) 24 (C) 54 (D) 72

3 Write an equation with the information given in each diagram below.

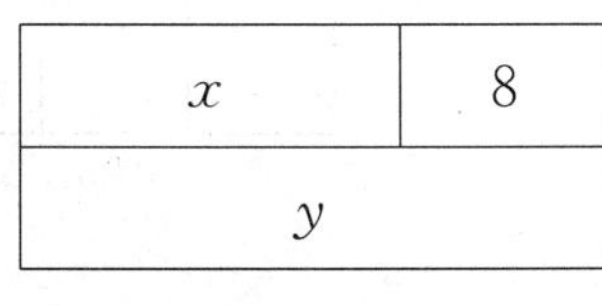

y	y	y	y
30			

______ = ______ ______ = ______

4 Write equations based on the relations between equal quantities.

(1) 2 times x equals 36. (2) The difference between 45 and x is 15.

(3) 12 more than 3 times x is 72.

(4) 48 is 2 times the sum of x and 3.

(5) Half of y is 25.

(6) 10 divided by 20 plus x is 8.

(7) 2 times x is 1 more than 3 times 5.

(8) 15 multiplied by 9 is 5 less than 4 times y.

Enhancement and extension

5 As shown in the diagram, the side length of the larger square is a cm, and the side length of the smaller square is b cm. Use expressions with letters to express the relationship between equal quantities involving a and b. What are the perimeter and the area of the larger rectangle? If a is 6 cm, find the length of b, the perimeter and the area of the larger rectangle.

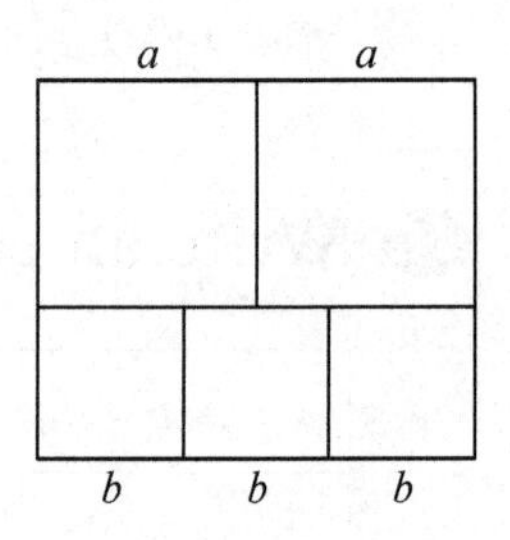

4.6 Equations (2)

Basic questions

1 Fill in the spaces.

(1) A value for the unknown that makes both sides of an equation equal is called (　　　　).

(2) (　　　　　　　　　　) to an equation is called solving the equation.

(3) The solution to equation $2y = 30$ is (　　　　).

(4) The solution to equation $x + 1.2 + 2.4 = 5$ is (　　　　).

2 Multiple choice questions.

(1) $x = 7$ is the solution to equation (　　).

(A) $x + 5 = 10$ 　　(B) $5 - x = 2$

(C) $3 + y = 10$ 　　(D) $37 - x = 30$

(2) In solving equation $0.25 \div x = 2.5$, the correct solution shown below is (　　).

(A) $0.25 \div x = 2.5$

Solution: $x = 2.5 \div 0.25$

$x = 10$

(B) $0.25 \div x = 2.5$

Solution: $= 0.25 \div 2.5$

$= 0.1$

(C) $0.25 \div x = 2.5$

Solution: $x = 0.25 \div 2.5$

$x = 0.1$

(D) $0.25 \div x = 2.5$

Solution: $x = 2.5 \times 0.25$

$x = 0.625$

3 Solve the equations. (Check the answers to the questions marked with $*$)

(1) $x + 8.25 = 11.39$ 　　(2) $72.6 - x = 36.8$

(3) $x - 2.4 = 2.4$ 　　(4) $0.25x = 0.4$

* (5) $x \div 3.6 = 0$ * (6) $x \div 2.6 = 2.6$

4 Write an equation based on each diagram below, and then find the solution to the equation.

(1) ________ Solution: ________
(2) ________ Solution: ________
(3) ________ Solution: ________
(4) ________ Solution: ________

Enhancement and extension

5 Write equations based on the diagram below, and find the values of x and y.

<table>
<tr><td colspan="2">x</td><td colspan="2">x</td><td colspan="2">x</td></tr>
<tr><td colspan="3">y</td><td colspan="3">y</td></tr>
<tr><td colspan="6">9.6</td></tr>
</table>

4.7 Equations (3)

Basic questions

1. Solve the equations. (Check the answers to the questions marked with *)

(1) $4x + 2.4 = 16.4$

(2) $7.8 - x \div 3 = 2.2$

(3) $7.2 - 0.3x = 1.8$

(4) $(6.8 + 1.2) \div x = 0.8$

(5) $18(3 + x) = 144$

(6) $(x + 8) \div 0.5 = 20$

(7) $14.8 - 5x = 3.3$

(8) $1.5(x - 2) = 7.5$

*(9) $3.6x - 7.8 = 4.8$

*(10) $(10 - x) \div 0.4 = 0.25$

2 Write the equations and then find the solutions.

(1) The sum of 4 times x and 3.2 is 9.8. Find x.

(2) 5 times the difference of 12 and x is 40. Find x.

(3) 102 less than 3 times x is 78. Find x.

(4) 5.4 is divided by the sum of x and 1.8, and the quotient is 2. Find x.

Enhancement and extension

3 Write equations based on the diagram and use reasoning to find the values of x and y.

<table>
<tr><td colspan="3">x</td><td colspan="3">x</td><td colspan="3">x</td><td colspan="3">x</td></tr>
<tr><td colspan="4">y</td><td colspan="4">y</td><td colspan="4">y</td></tr>
<tr><td colspan="3">x</td><td colspan="9">4.5</td></tr>
</table>

Equation: ________ $x =$ ________

Equation: ________ $y =$ ________

4.8 Equations (4)

Basic questions

1 Solve the equations. (Check the answers to the questions marked with *)

(1) $8x + 2 \times 1.5 = 21$

(2) $(15 + x - 8.4) \div 8 = 1.2$

(3) $9x - 3x + 1.2 = 10.2$

(4) $2.4(2x - 2.8) = 7.2$

(5) $1.6 + x = 3x$

(6) $25 \div (8x - 3x) = 2$

(7) $4.5x - 9 = 2.5x$

(8) $8x + 7.2 - 5x = 9$

*(9) $(12 - 3.6) \div (x + 1.1) = 2$

*(10) $x + 2x + 3 = 5x$

2 Write the equations and then find the solutions.

(1) The sum of 3.6 and x is multiplied by 4, and the product is 26.8. Find x.

(2) The sum of 1.6 times x and 2.4 times x is 10. Find x.

(3) 7 times x is equal to 4 times x plus 2.7. Find x.

(4) 8 times the result of subtracting x from 7.2 is exactly 4 times x. Find x.

Enhancement and extension

3 The number that is 2.4 more than 5 times x is exactly equal to the number that is 5.6 less than 9 times x. Find x.

4 Three people, A, B and C, went fishing in a suburban area and caught 60 fish altogether. Person A caught x fish, Person B caught twice as many fish as Person A, and Person C caught 3 times as many fish as Person A. Question: How many fish did Person A catch?

4.9 Writing equations to solve problems (1)

Basic questions

1 Solve the equations.

(1) $x \div 5 - 3 = 8$

(2) $6x + 1.5 = 4.5$

(3) $3x - x = 7.4$

(4) $2(x - 1.5) = 12$

2 Write equations and solve the application problems.

(1) There were 105 cars parked in a car park. After some cars drove away, it had 34 cars left. How many cars drove away?

(2) Xiao Pang read 98 pages of a book in total in two days. He read 55 pages on the first day. How many pages did he read on the second day?

(3) A school bought 480 ropes and gave them equally to 32 classes. How many ropes did each class receive?

(4) A school choir has 64 members, which is twice the number of members in the dancing group. How many members does the dancing group have?

(5) Subtracting 0.3 metres from 1.5 times the height of Xiao Pang gives his dad's height. Xiao Pang's dad is 1.8 metres tall. Question: What is Xiao Pang's height?

(6) The price of a pen divided by 4 and then plus 3 yuan is exactly the price of a ballpoint pen. The price of the ballpoint pen is 11.5 yuan. What is the price of the pen?

(7) Teacher Wang bought 1 football and 6 volleyballs at a total cost of 470 yuan. A volleyball costs 65 yuan. How much does a football cost?

(8) Mum bought 1 towel and 4 soap bars and paid 20 yuan. Given that a towel costs 6 yuan, how much does each soap bar cost?

Enhancement and extension

3 There are two pieces of wire. The first piece is 4.5 metres long. If 3.5 metres are cut off the second piece, the length of its remaining part is exactly 1.2 times the length of the first one. How many metres is the original length of the second piece?

4 The perimeter of a rectangle is 36 centimetres and the length is 11 centimetres. How many centimetres is the width?

4.10 Writing equations to solve problems (2)

Basic questions

1 Solve the equations.

(1) $7x - 3.5 = 9.1$

(2) $6x = 180 \div 4$

(3) $3(x + 2.3) = 9.6$

(4) $10x \div 2 - x = 6.4$

2 Write equations and solve application problems.

(1) In Shuguang Primary School, the number of members in the Chinese chess team multiplied by 4 and then added to 12 would be the same as the number of members in the tennis team. The tennis team has 80 members. How many members does the Chinese chess team have?

(2) A box of apples weighs 18 kilograms, which is 3 kilograms less than 1.5 times the weight of a box of oranges. What is the weight of a box of oranges?

(3) A pen costs 1.5 yuan more than 3 ballpoint pens. The price of a pen is 15 yuan. What is the price of a ballpoint pen?

(4) The length of the Yangzi River is 6300 kilometres, which is 4700 kilometres shorter than twice the length of the Yellow River. How many kilometres long is the Yellow River?

(5) A pizza topped with seafood costs 78 yuan, which is 14 yuan more than the price of two servings of spaghetti. How much is the price of 1 serving of spaghetti?

(6) Some people are doing physical exercises in a park. Among them, 28 people are doing exercise routines. If 8 more people join those doing exercise routines, the number of people doing exercise routines will be 3 times the number of people running. How many people are running?

(7) The Dalian Road Tunnel is 2565 metres long, 19 metres shorter than 4 times the length of the Bund Sightseeing Tunnel. How many metres long is the Bund Sightseeing Tunnel?

(8) Shanghai Unicom Company sells mobile phones. The number of sets of mobile phones it sold in the first month was 25 more than half of all the sets of mobile phones in stock. It sold 375 sets of mobiles phones in the first month. Question: How many sets of mobile phones were there in total in stock?

Enhancement and extension

❸ There are two warehouses, A and B. Warehouse A stored 50 tonnes of food at first. Then another 12 tonnes of food were shipped in to Warehouse A, while 16 tonnes of food were shipped out from Warehouse B. Now the amount of food in Warehouse A is twice the amount in Warehouse B. Question: How many tonnes of food did Warehouse B store at first?

4.11 Writing equations to solve problems (3)

Basic questions

1 Solve the equations.

(1) $90 - 5x = 35$

(2) $1.8x + 1.5x + 3.4 = 10$

(3) $(9x + 27) \div 2 = 81$

(4) $3x - 2(x + 1) = 8$

2 Write equations and solve application problems.

(1) A canteen received a delivery of 150 kilograms of rice, which was 30 kilograms less than 3 times the flour it received. How many kilograms of flour did the canteen receive?

(2) Warehouse A stored 56 tonnes of food, 8 tonnes more than twice the amount of the food stored in Warehouse B. How many tonnes of food did Warehouse B store?

(3) Mum is 35 years old this year, exactly 2 years more than 3 times Xiao Ya's age. How old is Xiao Ya this year?

(4) 36 white rabbits were on the grass, and then another 24 white rabbits joined in. By then there were 3 times as many white rabbits as black rabbits. How many black rabbits were on the grass?

(5) The capacity of a large drink bottle is 2.5 litres, 250 millilitres less than 5 times the capacity of a small drink bottle. How many millilitres is the capacity of the small bottle?

(6) Dad's age minus 4 and then divided by 3 is the son's age. The son is 12 years old this year. Quetsion: How old is Dad?

(7) Mr Li bought 72 metres of cloth, exactly enough to make 20 sets of adults' clothes and 16 sets of children's clothes. 2.4 metres of cloth is needed for each set of adult clothes. How many metres of cloth is needed for each set of children's clothes?

(8) There are 9 boxes of eggs, each with the same weight. If 15 kilograms of eggs are taken out from each box, the weight of the remaining eggs in the 9 boxes is 108 kilograms. What is the original weight of each box of eggs?

Enhancement and extension

❸ Three years ago, Mum's age was 6 times the age of the daughter. Mum is 33 years old this year. How old is the daughter this year?

Unit test 4

A. Calculation problems. (44 marks in total)

1 Solve the equations. (Check the answers to the questions marked with *)
(24 marks in total)

(1) $x - 2.3 = 2.7$

(2) $1.8 + 3x = 9.6$

(3) $25.2 - x \div 2 = 8$

* (4) $4x + 1.2 \times 5 = 24.4$

(5) $0.4(0.5x + 2) = 2.8$

(6) $2x - 8.6 + 0.5x = 5.4$

(7) $8x = 4x + 13.8$

* (8) $45 - 2(x - 2) = 19$

2 Simplify first and then evaluate. (8 marks in total)

(1) When $a = 4$, $b = 5$ and $c = 6$, find the value of $bc - ac$.

(2) When $a = 7$ and $b = 2.5$, find the value of $5a + 4b - (4a - 3b)$.

3 Write the equations and then find the solutions. (12 marks in total)

(1) The sum of 2.5 times a number and 5 is 25. Find the number.

(2) 6.5 times a number minus 4 times the number, the result is 12. Find the number.

(3) 8 times the difference of a number minus 5 and then divided by 3 equals 120. Find the number.

B. Application problems. (36 marks in total)

4 A canteen bought 8 kilograms of cucumbers. It paid 35 yuan and got 1.4 yuan change back. What was the price for each kilogram of cucumbers?

5 Xiao Ming has 55 science books and some storybooks. The number of science books is 14 less than 3 times the number of storybooks. How many storybooks does Xiao Ming have?

6 A construction team was paving a road. It paved 0.4 kilometres each day. After 8 days of work, it completed 0.5 kilometres more than half of the length of the road. How many kilometres is the length of the entire road?

7 A computer factory planned to assemble 5800 computers last month. In fact, 440 more computers than planned were assembled within 20 days. How many computers were assembled actually each day on average?

8 A factory has 800 female staff members. If the number of male staff members is reduced by 40, then the number of female staff members will be twice the number of male staff members. How many male staff members does the factory have?

9 There are two water ponds. Pond A has 40 tonnes of water. If 4 tonnes of water is poured into Pond A, and 8 tonnes of water is discharged from Pond B, then the amount of water in Pond A is twice the amount of water in Pond B. How many tonnes of water does Pond B have at first?

C. Concept problems. (20 marks in total)

(A) Fill in the brackets. (10 marks in total)

10 A road maintenance team repaired 2.4 kilometres of a highway in x days. It repaired (   ) kilometres each day on average.

11 Xiao Ming has a stamps, 3 stamps fewer than Xiao Hua. Xiao Hua has (   ) stamps.

12 Class 5(1) has a pupils. 3 pupils are taking leave today. (   ) pupils are present.

13 An orchard has x pear trees. The number of apple trees is 10 more than twice the number of pear trees. The orchard has ( ) apple trees.

14 If the unit price for 1 kilogram of apples is a yuan, then 3 kilograms of the apples will cost ( ) yuan. To buy 5 more kilograms of such apples, the total cost will be ( ).

15 A school has x boys, which is 24 more than the number of girls. There are ( ) pupils in the school in total. When $x = 652$, there are ( ) pupils in total.

16 If the perimeter of a square is $2a$ decimetres, then its area is ( ) square decimetres.

17 Xiao Ming, Xiao Jun and Xiao Gang had a 100-metre race. It took Xiao Ming x seconds. It took Xiao Jun 0.2 more seconds than Xiao Ming and it took Xiao Gang 0.3 seconds less than Xiao Jun. ( ) was the champion.

(B) True or false. (Put a "$\surd$" for true and a "$\times$" for false) (5 marks in total)

18 Both t^2 and $2t$ represent t times t. ( )

19 An expression does not necessarily mean an equation while an equation must involve an expression. ( )

20 Simplify: $5x - 4x - 9 + 8 = x - 17$. ( )

21 A value for the unknown that makes both sides of an equation equal is called a solution to the equation. ( )

22 Three people, A, B and C, went to buy sports goods with the same amount of money. Person A bought 3 footballs, Person B bought 4 basketballs, and Person C bought 1 football, 1 basketball and 2 volleyballs. If each football costs $4x$ yuan, then each volleyball costs $2.5x$ yuan. ( )

(C) **Multiple choice questions.** (5 marks in total)

23 In the following, ( ) is an equation.

(A) $25x$ (B) $15-3=12$ (C) $6x+1=6$ (D) $4x+7<9$

24 $x=3$ is the solution to the equation ( ).

(A) $3x=4.5$ (B) $2x+9=5x$ (C) $1.2\div x=4$ (D) $3x\div 2=18$

25 Five squares with side length a are put together to form a large rectangle. The perimeter of the large rectangle is ( ).

(A) $5a$ (B) $10a$ (C) $12a$ (D) $20a$

26 Grade 5 pupils planted a trees, which were b trees fewer than twice the number of trees the Grade 4 pupils planted. Grade 4 pupils planted ( ) trees.

(A) $(2a-b)$ (B) $(a+b)\div 2$ (C) $2(a+b)$ (D) $(a-b)\div 2$

27 If $2a+2b+1=6$, then the result of $5(a+b)-4$ is ( ).

(A) 2.5 (B) 4.5 (C) 8.5 (D) 12.5

Chapter 5 Let's practise geometry

5.1 Parallelograms (1)

Basic questions

1 In the diagram, (　　)//(　　), (　　)//(　　). A quadrilateral like this in which two pairs of opposite sides are (　　　) to each other is called a (　　　). AC and BD are both called (　　　) of $\square ABCD$.

Diagram for Question 1

2 The opposite sides of a parallelogram are parallel to each other, and their lengths are (　　　). The opposite angles are also (　　　).

3 A parallelogram with one angle a right angle is a (　　　).

4 A rectangle with all four sides of equal length is a (　　　).

5 Both (　　　) and (　　　) are special parallelograms.

6 In the following figures, the parallelogram(s) is/are (　　　).

Diagram for Question 6

7 When the four sides of a parallelogram are determined, its shape and size (　　　) completely determined. (Fill in with "are" or "are not")

8 True or false. (Put a "√" for true and a "×" for false)

(1) A parallelogram can be cut into two identical triangles along its

diagonal. ( )

(2) The opposite angles in a parallelogram are equal and are right angles. ( )

(3) A quadrilateral with all four sides of equal length is called a square. ( )

(4) The total length of the four sides of a parallelogram is its perimeter. ( )

(5) A parallelogram is a symmetrical figure with a line of symmetry. ( )

9 Look at the diagram as shown, and draw the parallelograms as indicated in the diagram.

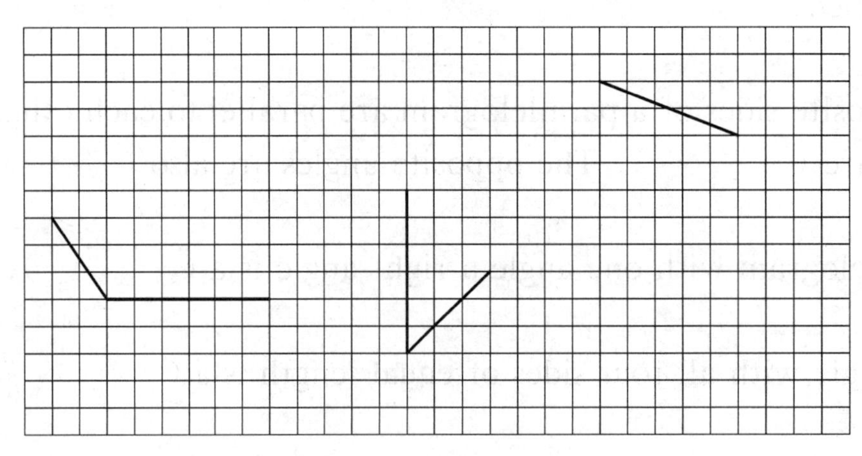

Diagram for Question 9

10 Multiple choice questions.

(1) The shape that has stability is a ( ).

(A) triangle (B) square

(C) rectangle (D) parallelogram

(2) Cut a parallelogram along its two diagonals to get four triangles. They may be ( ).

(A) four acute-angled triangles

(B) two right-angled triangles and two obtuse-angled triangles

(C) four obtuse-angled triangles

(D) two acute-angled triangles and two obtuse-angled triangles

Enhancement and extension

11 As shown in the diagram, how many parallelograms are there in the figure?

Diagram for Question 11

12 There are six small sticks with different lengths: 1 centimetre, 2 centimetres, 3 centimetres, 5 centimetres, 6 centimetres and 7 centimetres. To use these six small sticks to form a parallelogram, the opposite sides of the parallelogram will be (   ) and (   ), or (   ) and (   ).

5.2 Parallelograms (2)

Basic questions

1. In the diagram, MN is the ( ) on side DC of the parallelogram, and side DC is called the ( ) of the parallelogram.

2. Draw a perpendicular line from a point on one side of a parallelogram. The line segment between this point and the perpendicular foot is called the ( ) on the base of the parallelogram.

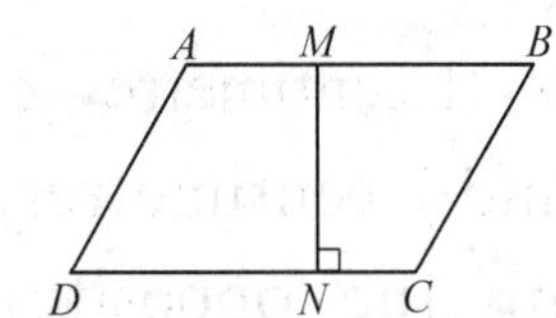

Diagram for Question 1

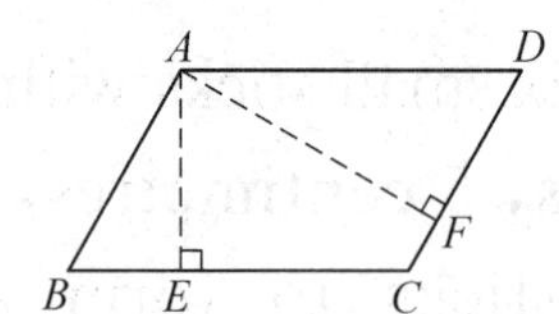

Diagram for Question 3

3. The figure shows a parallelogram $ABCD$. If the base is AB, then the height is ( ). If the height is AE, then the base is ( ) or ( ).

4. The lengths of all the heights on one side of a parallelogram are ( ).

5. The figure shows a parallelogram. The height in the figure should be ( ) or ( ).

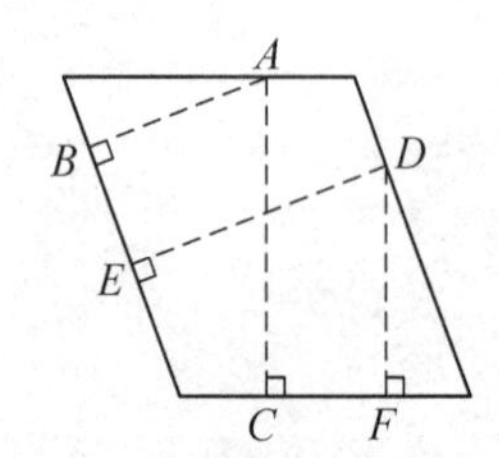

Diagram for Question 5

6. Passing through a point on the base of a parallelogram, at most ( ) height(s) can be drawn.

7. If two pairs of opposite sides of a quadrilateral are parallel to each other, and one of the angles is a right angle, then the quadrilateral is called a ( ); it is also called a special ( ).

8. Multiple choice questions.
   (1) The base of parallelogram $ABCD$ is AB, and its height is ( ).
   (A) CD (B) AE (C) DF (D) BC

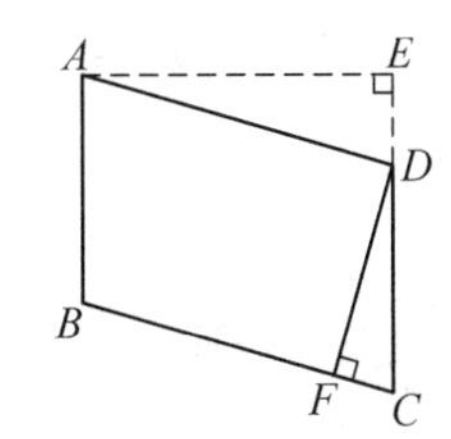

Figure for Question 8 (1)

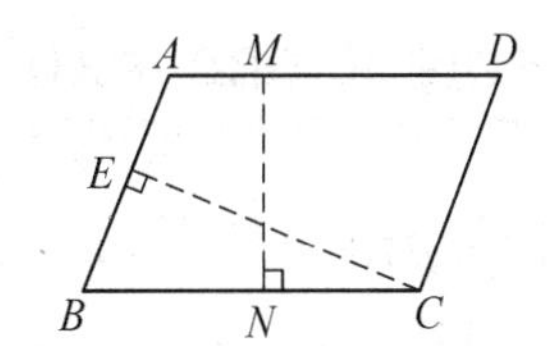

Figure for Question 8 (2)

(2) In parallelogram $ABCD$, (　　) do not have the relation of a base and its height.

(A) AB and CE　　(B) BC and MN

(C) AD and CD　　(D) CD and CE

(3) On a side of a parallelogram, (　　) heights can be drawn.

(A) 1　　(B) 2　　(C) 4　　(D) infinitely many

9 Draw 3 different parallelograms on the grid paper (assume the side length of each grid is 1 cm), each with base 3 cm and height 2 cm.

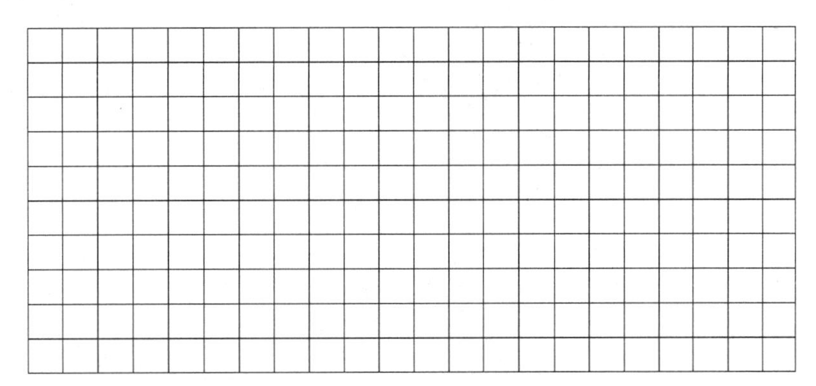

Diagram for Question 9

10 As shown in the diagram, draw the height of each parallelogram on the base indicated.

(1) 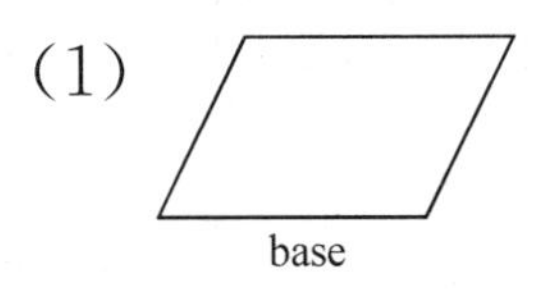

(2) 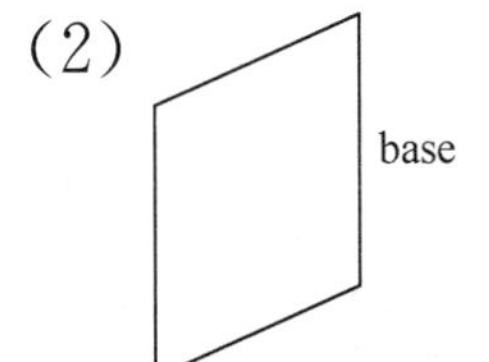

(3) 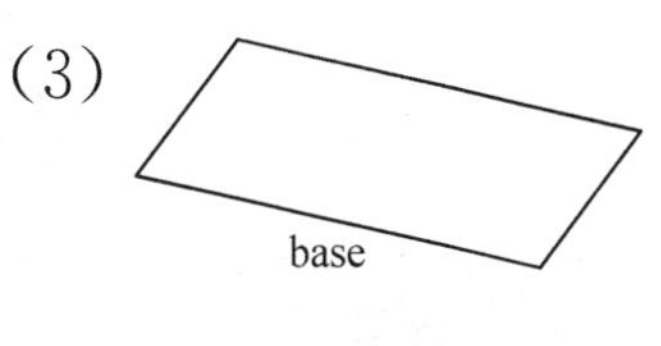

Diagram for Question 10

Enhancement and extension

11 In parallelogram $ABCD$, AB is 6 cm and BC is 8 cm. The height AE can be (   ) cm.

(A) 5   (B) 6   (C) 7

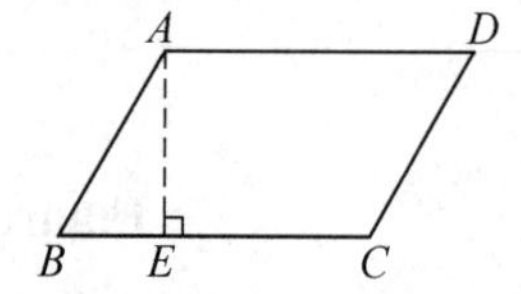

Diagram for Question 11

12 The perimeter of parallelogram $ABCD$ is 50 cm and AB is 15 cm. Then BC is (   ) cm.

13 Let's count. How many parallelograms are there in the figure below?

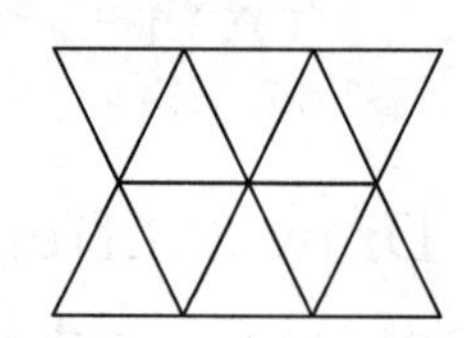

Diagram for Question 13

5.3 Area of a parallelogram

Basic questions

1 Fill in the table.

Parallelogram	Base	3.2 m	2.4 dm	1.8 dm	2.5 cm
	Height	1.5 m	7 dm		
	Area			0.9 dm^2	8 cm^2

2 Calculate the areas of the following parallelograms. (unit: cm)

(1) 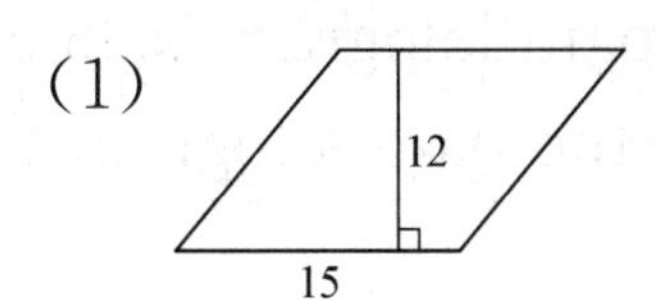

(2) 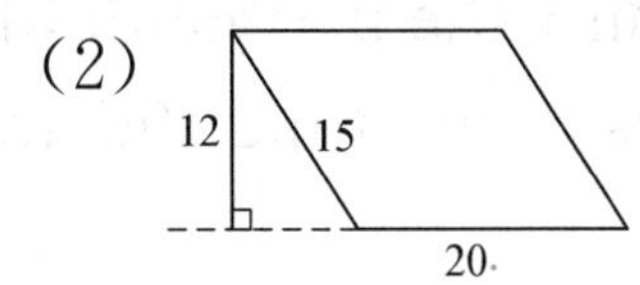

(3) 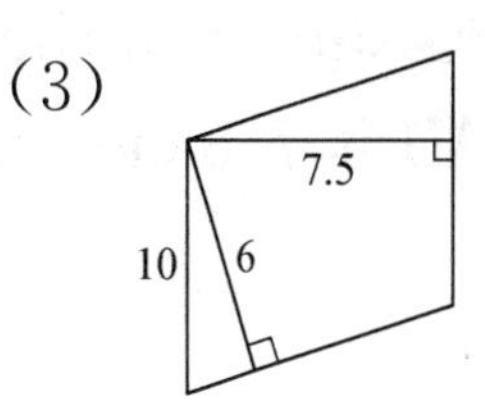

3 Multiple choice questions.

(1) As shown in the diagram, to calculate the area of the parallelogram, the correct one is (　　). (unit: cm)

(A) 5×6　　(B) 8×4　　(C) 8×5　　(D) 4×5

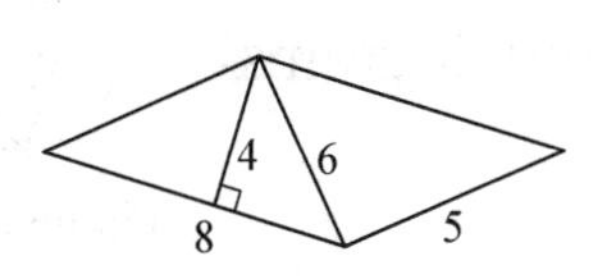

Diagram for Question 3(1)

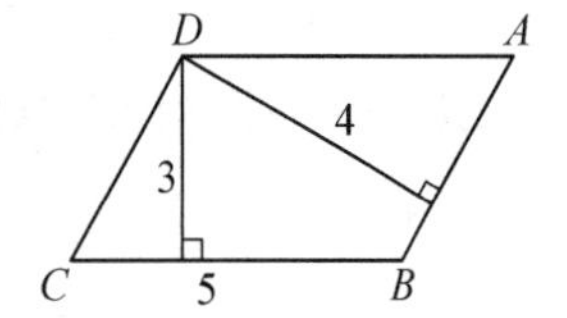

Diagram for Question 3(2)

(2) As shown in the diagram, to find the length of CD, the correct one is (　　). (unit: cm)

(A) $5\times4\div3$　　(B) $3\times4\div5$　　(C) $5\times3\div4$　　(D) $5\times3\times4$

4 Application problems.

(1) The area of a parallelogram is 10.8 m^2 and its height is 2.4 m. Find the length of the base corresponding to the height.

(2) The base of a parallelogram is 4.5 dm, which is 1.3 dm more than its height. Find the area.

(3) Yucai Primary School has a piece of open space in the shape of parallelogram with base 28 metres and height 15 metres. This open space is to be covered with turf. If the turf costs 45 yuan per square metre, what is the total cost to cover the whole area?

(4) As shown in the diagram, the perimeter of the parallelogram is 36 cm, AB is 7.8 cm and AE is 5 cm. Find the area of the parallelogram.

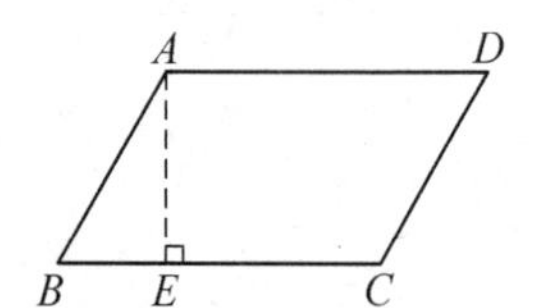

Figure for Question 4 (4)

Enhancement and extension

5 As shown in the diagram, the relationship between the areas of the shaded parts in the two parallelograms, A and B, is ( ).

(A) $A > B$ (B) $A = B$

(C) $A < B$ (D) uncertain

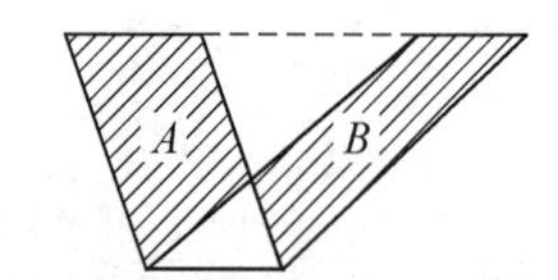

Diagram for Question 5

6 In the diagram, $EF \parallel AD$, $BE \parallel CG$, $BF \parallel AG$ and $CE \parallel DF$. Write the parallelograms that have the same areas. (Use letters to represent the parallelograms)

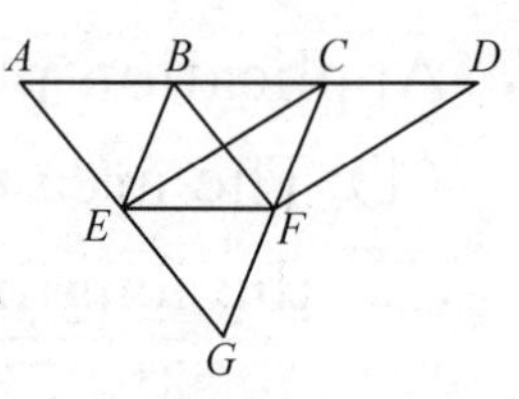

Diagram for Question 6

5. 4 Area of a triangle (1)

Basic questions

1 Fill in the table.

Triangle	Base	1. 5 m	2. 7 dm	0. 44 m	1. 25 cm
	Height	1. 2 m	0. 8 dm	0. 15 m	3. 6 cm
	Area				

2 In the diagram, draw the height to the given base of each triangle.

(1)

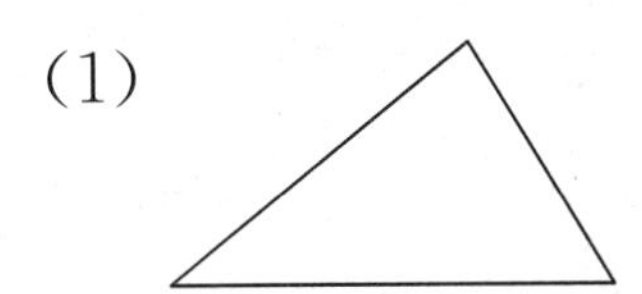

(2)

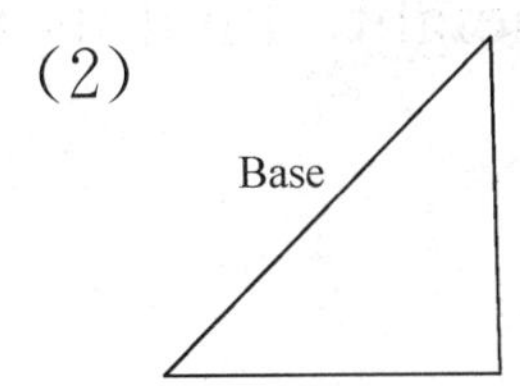

(3)

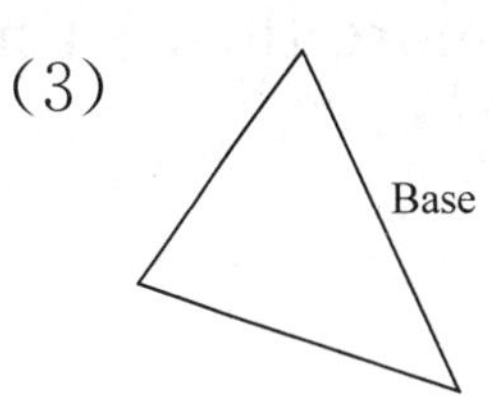

Diagram for Question 2

3 Fill in the brackets.

The diagram shows $\triangle ABC$. The corresponding height to base AC is (　　　　), the corresponding base to height AD is (　　　　), and the corresponding height to base (　　　　) is (　　　　).

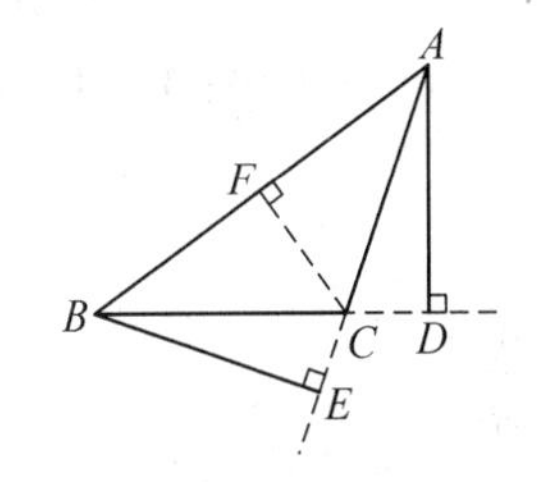

Diagram for Question 3

4 Look at each figure as shown in the diagram. Find the area of each triangle. (unit: cm)

(1)

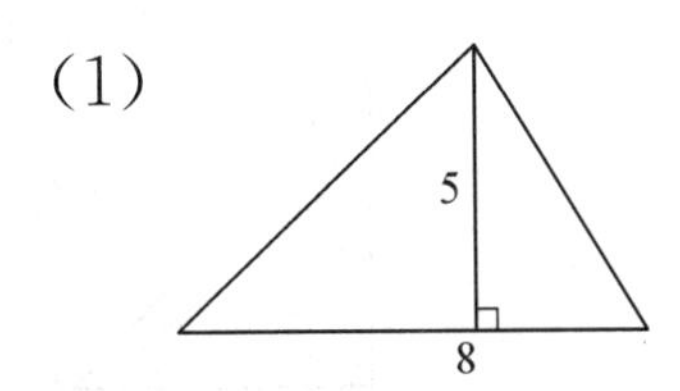

(2)

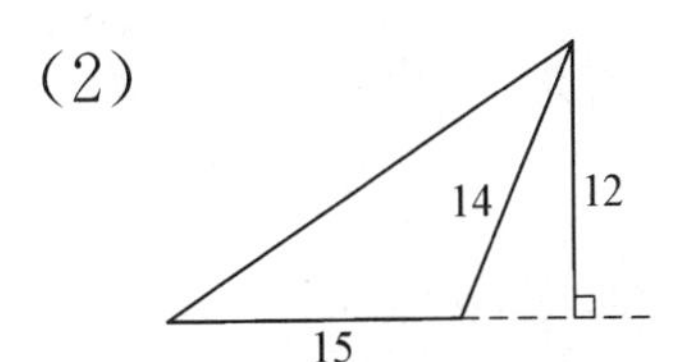

(3)

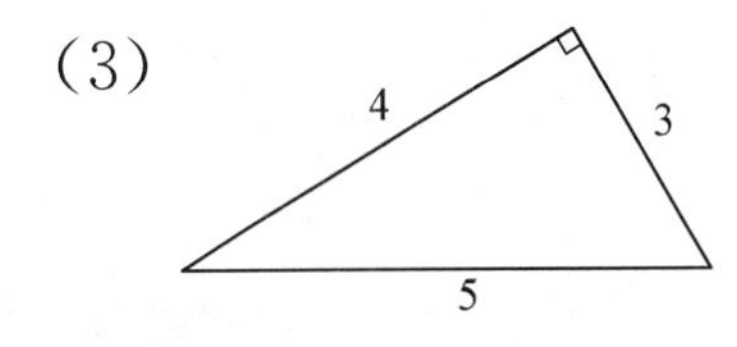

Diagram for Question 4

5 True or false. (Put a "√" for true and a "×" for false)

(1) The area of a triangle is half the area of a parallelogram. (　　)

(2) There is only one height in an obtuse-angled triangle. (　　)

(3) There are three pairs of corresponding base and height in a triangle. ( )

(4) In a right-angled triangle, if the lengths of the two sides of the right angle are given, then its area can be found. ( )

6 Application problems.

(1) In a triangle, the base is 18 decimetres, twice the height. Find its area.

(2) In a triangle, the height is 24 centimetres and the base is 3 centimetres more than 3 times the height. Find its area.

(3) In a triangle, the base is 32 centimetres, 7 centimetres more than the height. How many square decimetres is its area?

Enhancement and extension

7 In a right-angled triangle ABC, $\angle A = 45^\circ$ and $BC = 6$ cm. Find its area.

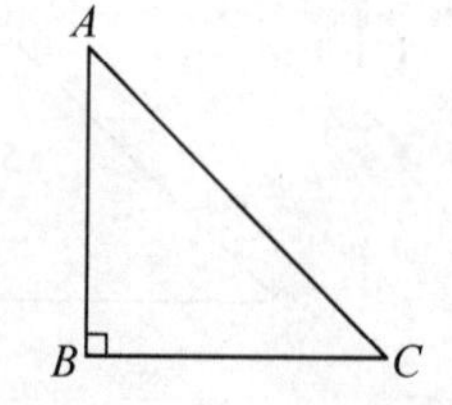

Diagram for Question 7

8 In a right-angled triangle, the side lengths are 3.6 cm, 4.8 cm and 6 cm. Find its area.

5.5 Area of a triangle (2)

Basic questions

1 Calculate the area of each triangle below. (unit: cm)

(1)

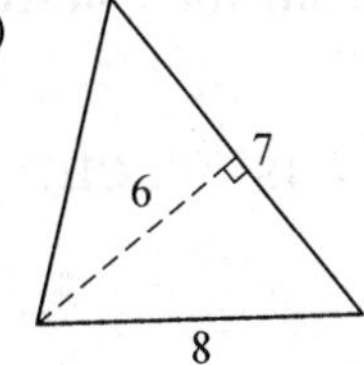

(2)

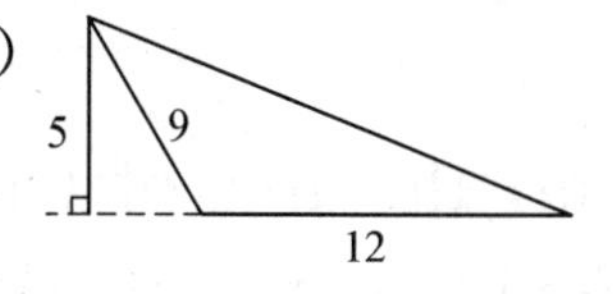

(3)

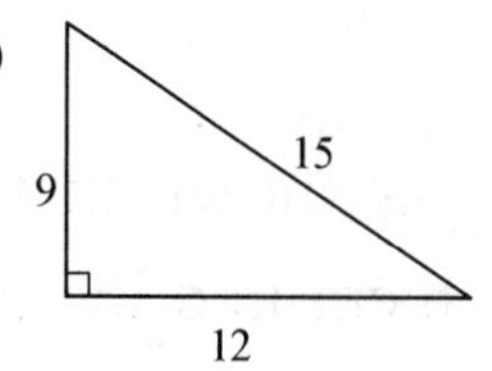

Diagram for Question 1

2 As shown in the diagram, find the unknown in each triangle below.

(1) $S = 20\ \text{cm}^2$　　(2) $S = 32.4\ \text{m}^2$　　(3) $S = 15.36\ \text{dm}^2$

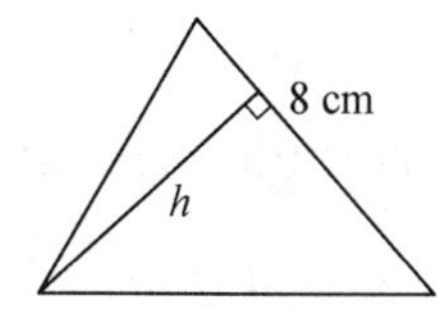

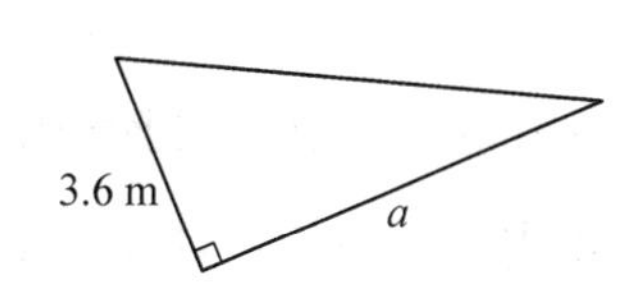

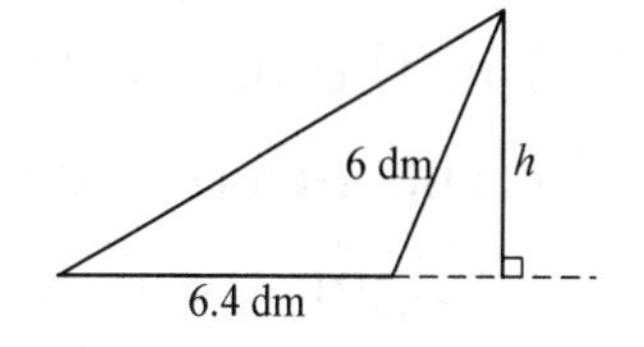

Diagram for Question 2

3 Application problems.

(1) The height of a triangular flowerbed is 18 m, which is 8 m less than its corresponding base. What is the area of the flowerbed?

(2) There is a triangular vegetable plot with base 24 m and height 16 m. If the base is increased by 6 m and the height is increased by 3 m, by how many square metres will the area of the plot be increased?

(3) As shown in the diagram, the area of rectangle $ABCD$ is 66 dm^2, AB is 6 dm and BE is 4 dm. Find the area of triangle CDE.

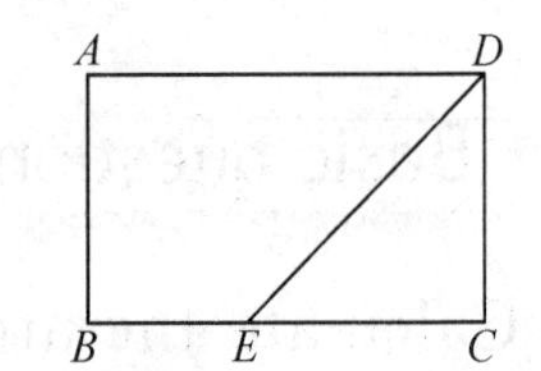

Diagram for Question 3(3)

(4) As shown in the diagram, the area of triangle ABD is 24 cm^2, BD is 6 cm and DC is 5 cm. Find the area of triangle ABC.

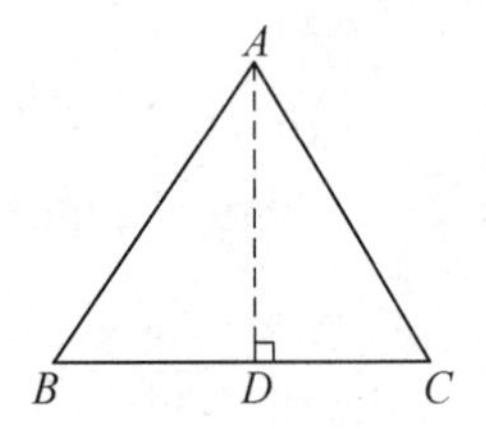

Diagram for Question 3(4)

4 Fill in the brackets.

(1) The area of a parallelogram is 10 m^2. The area of a triangle whose base and height are equal to the base and the height of the parallelogram is (　　　) m^2

(2) If the base of a triangle is increased to twice its original length, and the height is increased to 3 times its original length, then the area is increased to (　　　) times the original area.

(3) The area of a triangle is the same as the area of a parallelogram and their heights are equal as well. If the base of the parallelogram is 10 dm, then the base of the triangle is (　　) dm.

(4) As shown in the diagram, in the right-angled triangle ABC, $AB = 3$ cm, $BC = 4$ cm and $AC = 5$ cm, then $BD =$ (　　　) cm

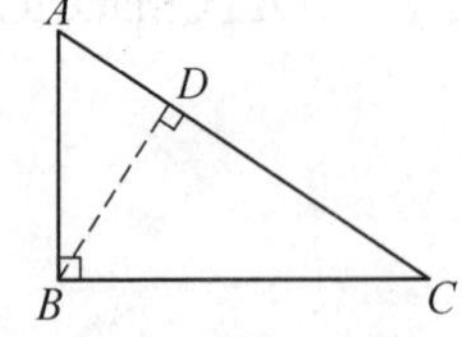

Diagram for Question 4(4)

Enhancement and extension

5 What is the sum of the areas of the shaded parts in the diagram?

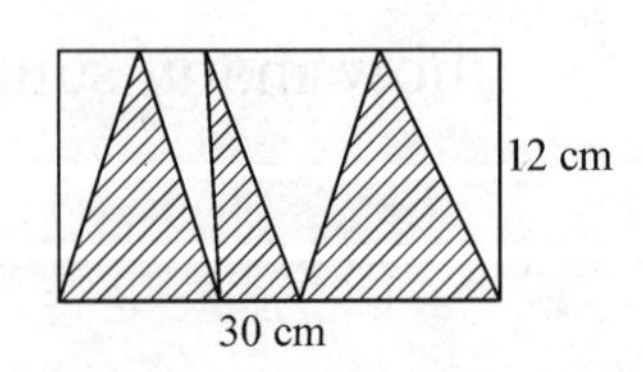

Diagram for Question 5

5.6 Trapezia

Basic questions

1 Fill in the brackets.

(1) A quadrilateral with only one pair of opposite sides parallel is called a (　　).

(2) A trapezium with one angle a right angle is called a (　　　　　　).
A trapezium with two lateral sides equal is called an (　　　　　　).

(3) Draw a perpendicular line from one point on the top base downwards, the segment between this point and the perpendicular foot is called the (　　　　) of the trapezium.

(4) The figure that can be obtained by extending the two lateral sides of a trapezium is a (　　　　).

2 There are (　　　　) trapezia in the diagram below.

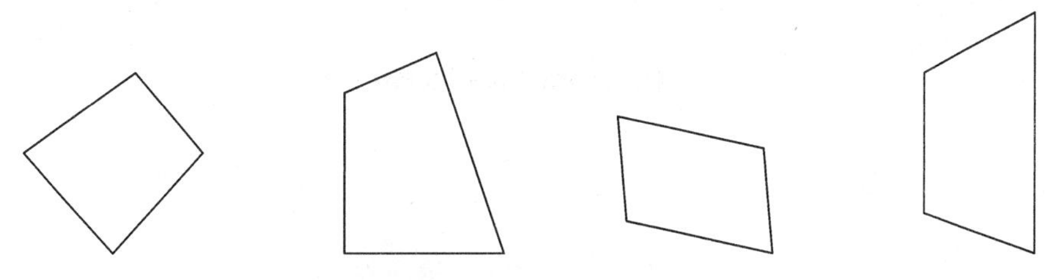

Diagram for Question 2

3 On the grid below (assume the side length is 1 cm), three trapezia are drawn. Fill in the brackets according to their features.

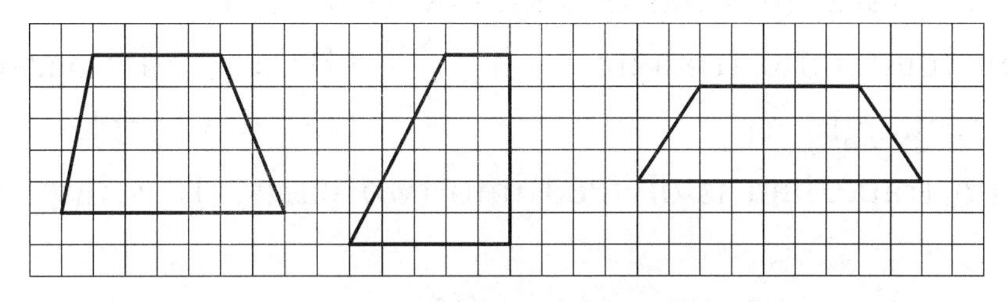

Diagram for Question 3

In the first trapezium, the top base is (　　　) cm, the bottom base is (　　　), and the height is (　　　) cm.
In the right-angled trapezium, the top base is (　　　　) cm, the bottom

base is (　　　　), and the height is (　　　　) cm.
In the isosceles trapezium, the top base is (　　　　) cm, the bottom base is (　　　　), and the height is (　　　　) cm.

4 True or false. (Put a "√" for true and a "×" for false)

(1) A figure with only one pair of opposite sides parallel is called a trapezium. (　　)

(2) The shorter lateral side of a right-angled trapezium is the height. (　　)

(3) Infinitely many heights can be drawn in a trapezium. (　　)

(4) The length of the top base in a trapezium does not equal the length of its bottom base. (　　)

5 As shown in the diagram, draw a height of each trapezium.

(1)　　　(2)　　　(3)

Diagram for Question 5

6 Multiple choice questions.

(1) Two identical trapezia can definitely form a (　　).

(A) triangle　　(B) parallelogram
(C) rectangle　　(D) square

(2) A quadrilateral that has one symmetrical line is (　　).

(A) an equilateral triangle　　(B) a parallelogram
(C) a rectangle　　(D) an isosceles trapezium

(3) When a trapezium is divided into two parts. It is impossible to have (　　).

(A) two triangles
(B) a parallelogram and a triangle
(C) two parallelograms
(D) two right-angled trapezia

Enhancement and extension

7 How many trapezia are there in the figure?

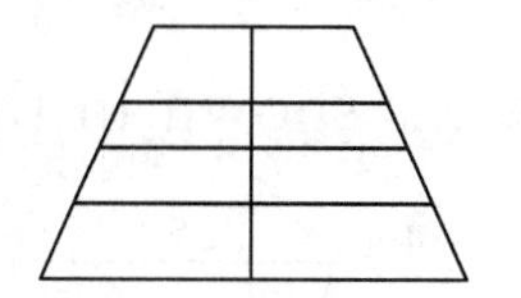

Diagram for Question 7

8 Put a "√" for a correct answer and a "×" for an incorrect answer. A right-angled trapezium is divided into two parts, and they may be

(1) an obtuse-angled triangle and a right-angled triangle. ( )
(2) a rectangle and a triangle. ( )
(3) a trapezium and a parallelogram. ( )
(4) an obtuse-angled triangle and an acute-angled triangle. ( )
(5) a rectangle and a right-angled trapezium. ( )
(6) a parallelogram and an obtuse-angled triangle. ( )

5.7 Area of a trapezium (1)

Basic questions

1 As shown in the diagram, find the area of each trapezium. (unit: cm)

(1) 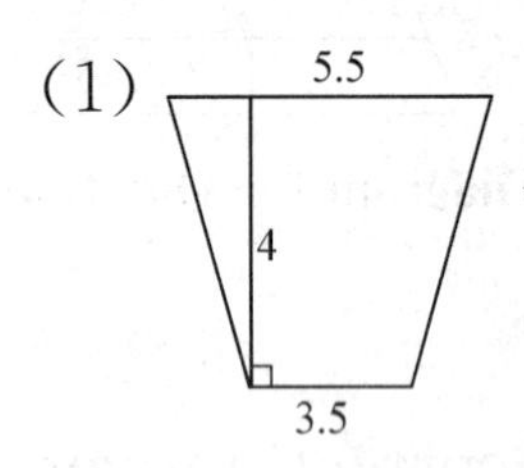

(2) 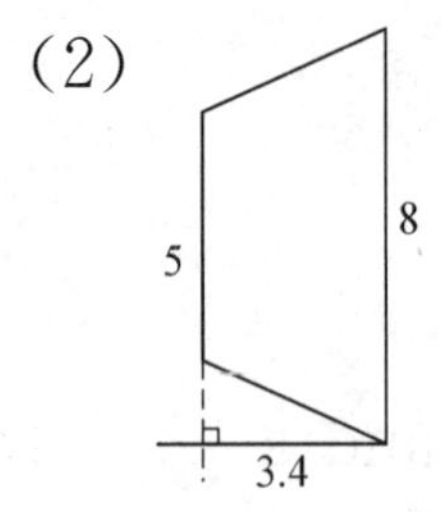

(3) 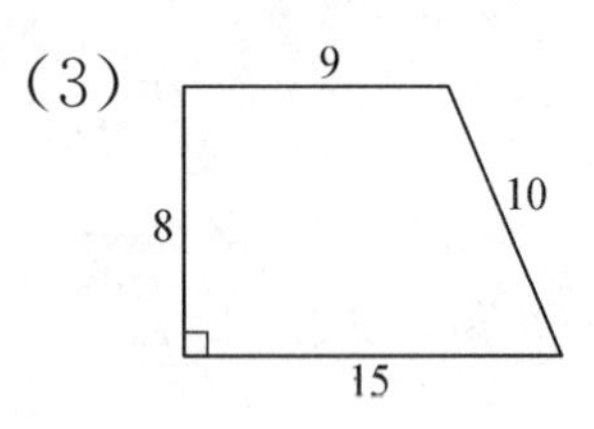

Diagram for Question 1

2 Fill in the brackets.

(1) When a parallelogram with area 100 cm^2 is divided into two identical trapezia, the area of each trapezium is (　　　　) cm^2.

(2) The top base of a trapezium is 7.5 cm, 3 cm shorter than the bottom base, and the height is 6 cm. Its area is (　　　　) cm^2.

(3) The sum of the top and bottom bases of a trapezium is 12 dm, twice the length of the height. Then its area is (　　　　) dm^2.

(4) The top base of a trapezium is 6 metres, the bottom base is 10 metres, and the height is 9 metres. If a maxium parallelogram is cut out from the trapezium, the remaining figure is a (　　　　) and the area is (　　　　) square metres.

(5) In a trapezium, the top base is 6.8 dm, half the length of the bottom base. The height is 3.6 dm less than the bottom base. Then the area of the trapezium is (　　　　) dm^2.

3 Multiple choice questions.

(1) Two trapezia with (　　) can form a parallelogram.

(A) the same shape

(B) the equal area

(C) the top bases, the bottom bases, and the heights all equal

(D) the same shape and the equal area

(2) As shown in the diagram, to calculate the area of the trapezium, the correct expression is ( ).

(A) $(12+28)\times 10$

(B) $(12+28)\times 22\div 2$

(C) $(12+28)\times 14\div 2$

(D) $(12+28)\times 10\div 2$

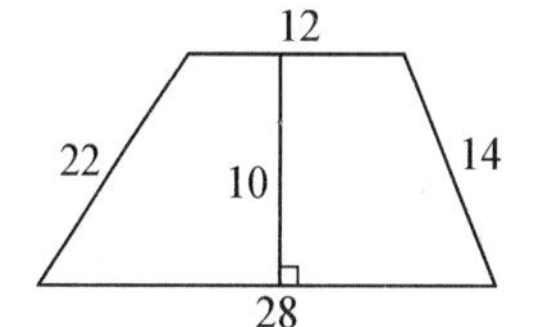

Diagram for Question 3(2)

4 Application problems.

(1) There is a trapezium-shaped piece of farmland. The top base is 20 metres, the bottom base is 28 metres, and the height is 15 metres. How many square metres is the area of this farmland?

(2) There is a trapezium-shaped piece of land. The top base is 17 metres, the bottom base is 1 metre less than twice the length of the top base and 3 times the height. Find the area of the plot.

(3) A steel company received a batch of steel tubes, which were stacked in a trapezium shape. There were 10 tubes at the top layer and 20 tubes at the bottom layer with a total of 11 layers. The difference between each two adjacent layers is 1 tube. If the price of each steel tube was 500 yuan, how much was the total value of all the steel tubes?

Enhancement and extension

5 The perimeter of an isosceles trapezium is 30 cm, the length of one lateral side is 5 cm and the height is 4 cm. Find its area.

5.8 Area of a trapezium (2)

Basic questions

1 Fill in the table.

Top base (cm)	2.4	4	3.32	1.9
Bottom base (cm)	2.8	6	4.48	
Height (cm)	3		5	3.2
Area (cm^2)		15		7.36

2 As shown in the diagram, calculate the unknown of each trapezium.

(1)

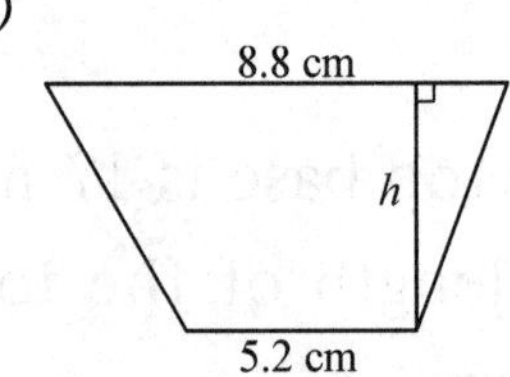

Diagram for Question 2(1)

$S = 42\ cm^2$, find h.

(2)

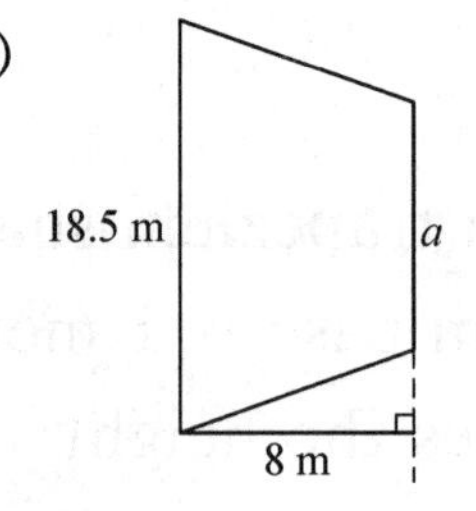

Diagram for Question 2(2)

$S = 120\ m^2$, find a.

3 Application problems.

(1) The cross section of a canal is a trapezium. Its area is 1.52 square metres, the depth is 0.8 metres, and the bottom base is 1.4 metres. How many metres is the length of the top base?

(2) The top base of a trapezium is 5.6 centimetres, 1.4 centimetres shorter than its bottom base. The area is 20.16 square centimetres. How many centimetres is its height?

(3) Two squares with lengths 4 cm and 3 cm are placed as shown in the diagram. Find the area of each shaded part.

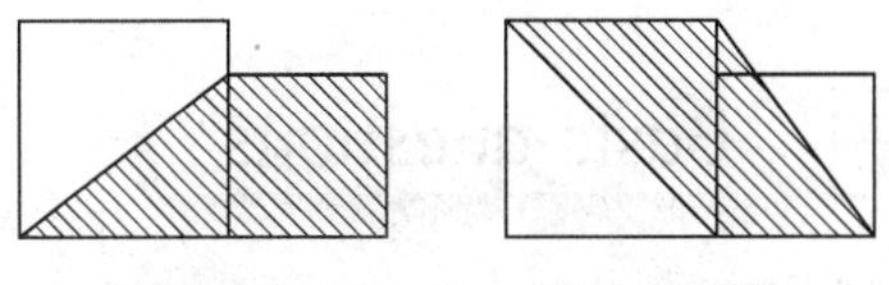
Diagram for Question 3(3)

(4) The area of a trapezium is 128 cm^2, the height is 8 cm, and the bottom base is 4 cm more than the top base. How many centimetres is the top base?

(5) As shown in the diagram, in the right-angled trapezium $ABCD$, AD is 12 cm, BC is 16 cm, and the area of triangle ACD is 60 cm^2. Find the area of the right-angled trapezium.

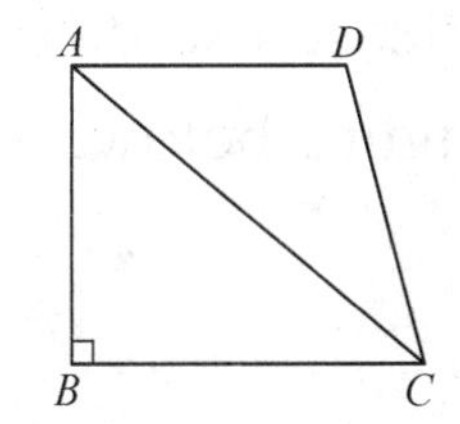

Diagram for Question 3(5)

Enhancement and extension

4 In a right-angled trapezium, if the top base is extended by 5 cm, the bottom base is extended by 2 cm, and the height remains unchanged, then the area is increased by 28 cm^2 and it becomes a square. Find the area of the original right-angled trapezium.

5.9 Areas of composite figures

Basic questions

1. Try different ways of calculation to find the area of each composite figure below. (unit: cm)

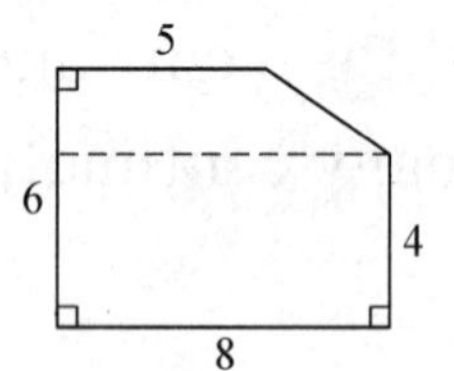

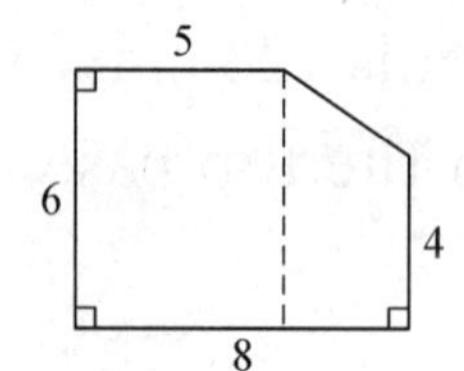

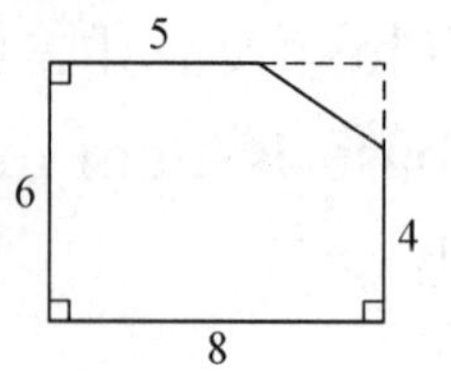

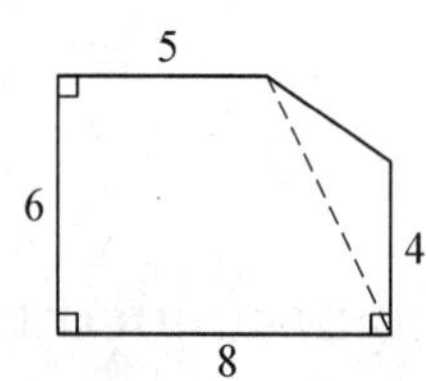

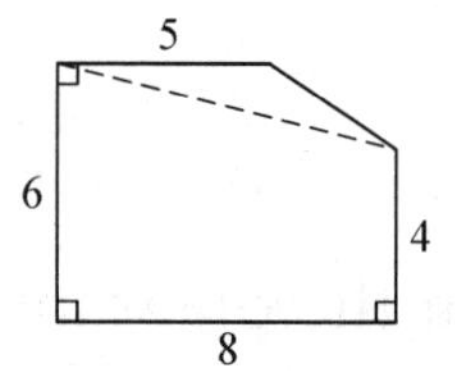

2. Please use different ways of calculation to find the area of the composite figure below. (unit: cm)

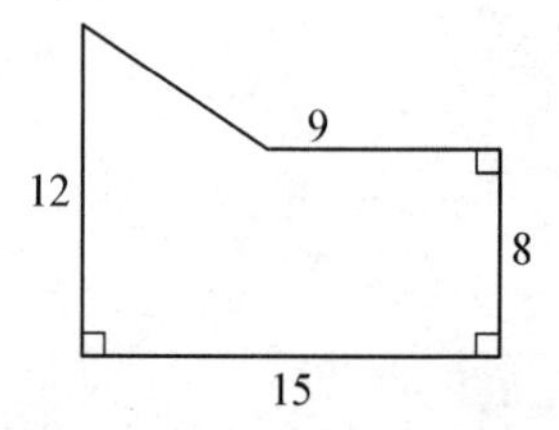

Diagram for Question 2

3. As shown in the diagram, find the area of each composite figure below. (unit: cm)

(1)

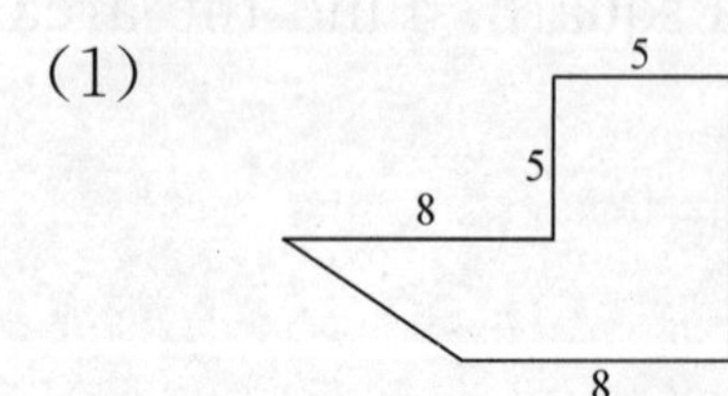

Diagram for Question 3(1)

(2)

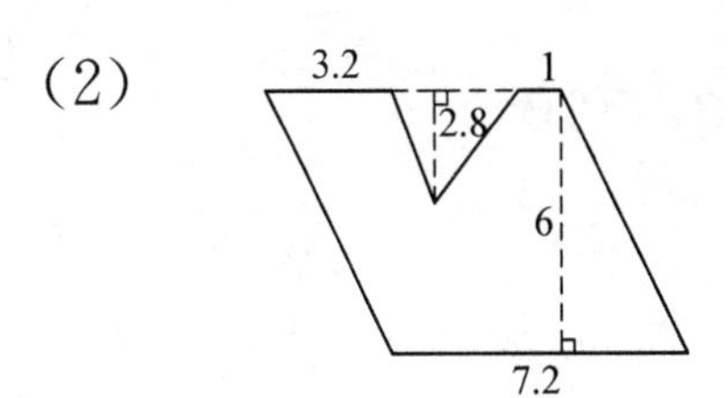

Diagram for Question 3(2)

(3)

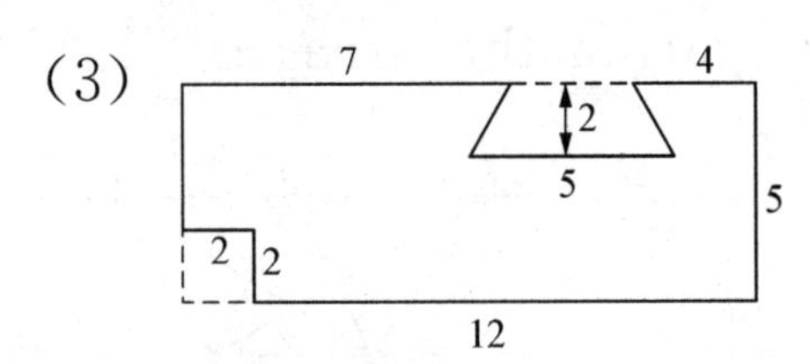

Diagram for Question 3(3)

Enhancement and extension

4 Find the area of the shaded part in each diagram below. (unit: dm)

(1)

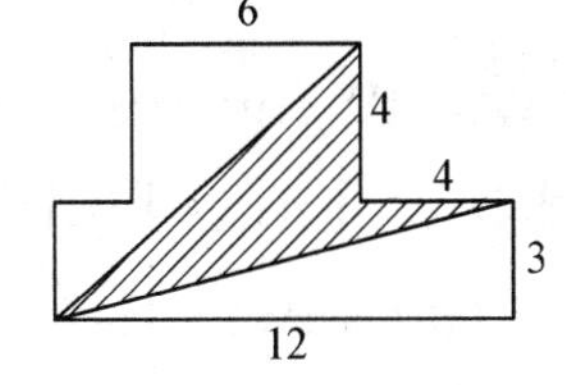

Diagram for Question 4(1)

(2)

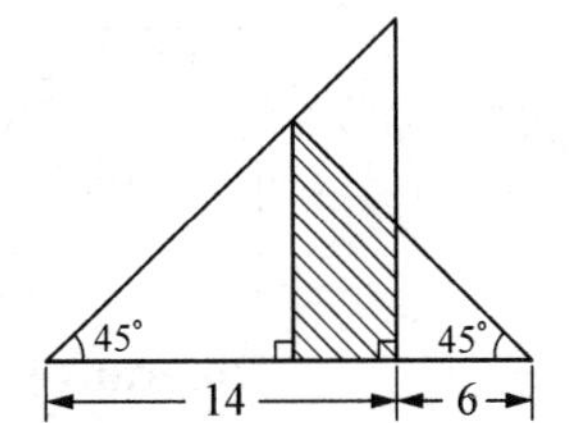

Diagram for Question 4(2)

5.10 Practice and exercise

Basic questions

1 Multiple choice questions.

(1) As shown in the diagram, $a \parallel b$, comparing the areas of $\triangle ABC$, $\triangle EBC$ and $\triangle FBC$, the result is (   ).

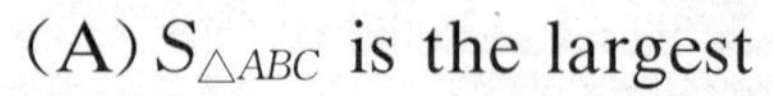

(A) $S_{\triangle ABC}$ is the largest

(B) $S_{\triangle EBC}$ is the largest

(C) $S_{\triangle FBC}$ is the largest

(D) All the areas are the same.

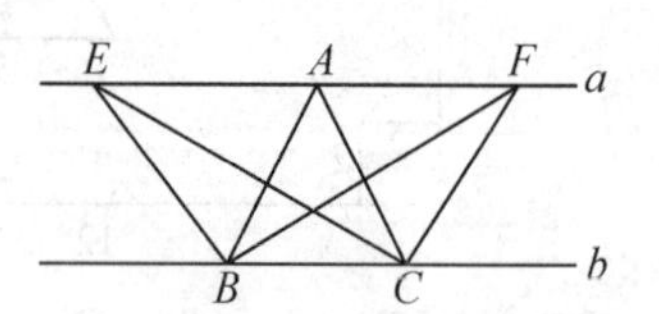

Diagram for Question 1(1)

(2) A parallelogram and a trapezium have the same area and the same height. The base of the parallelogram is $2a$, and the top base of the trapezium is a. Then the bottom base of the trapezium is (   ).

(A) a (B) $2a$ (C) $3a$ (D) $5a$

2 As shown in the diagram, in a rectangular lawn 40 metres long and 30 metres wide, there are two paths each with width 2 metres built across the lawn. How many square metres is the area of the lawn after the paths were built?

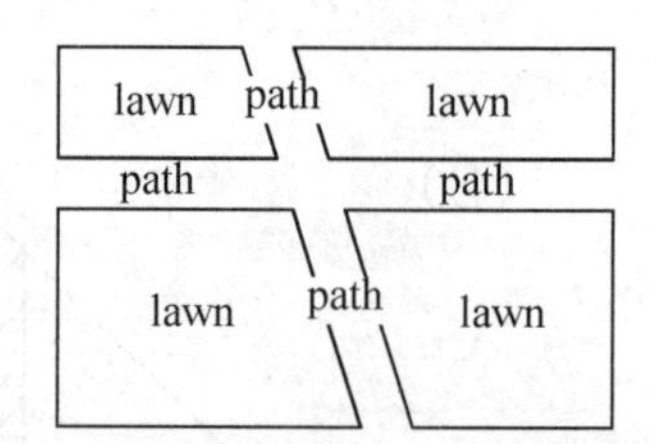

Diagram for Question 2

3 As shown in the diagram, Aunt Wang built a trapezium-shaped enclosure with a 20-metre-long fence and a wall for raising chickens. What is the area of this land of enclosure?

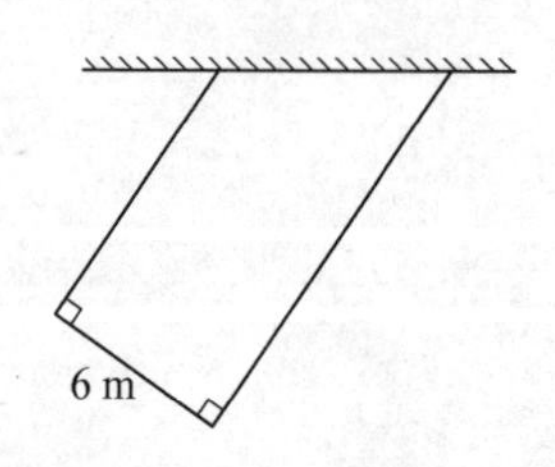

Diagram for Question 3

4 As shown in the diagrams, find the area of each composite figure below. (unit: cm)

(1)

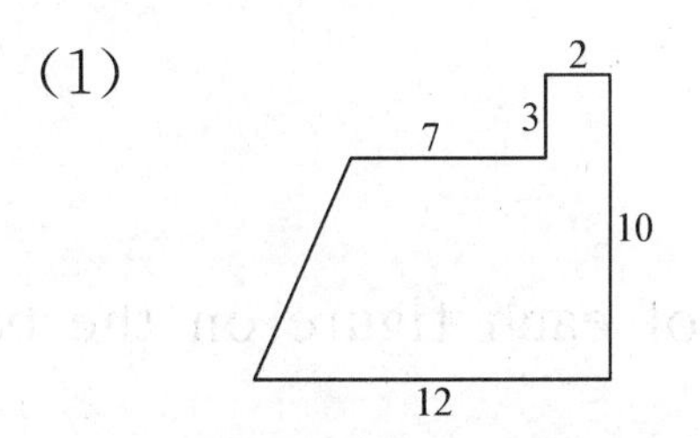

Diagram for Question 4(1)

(2)

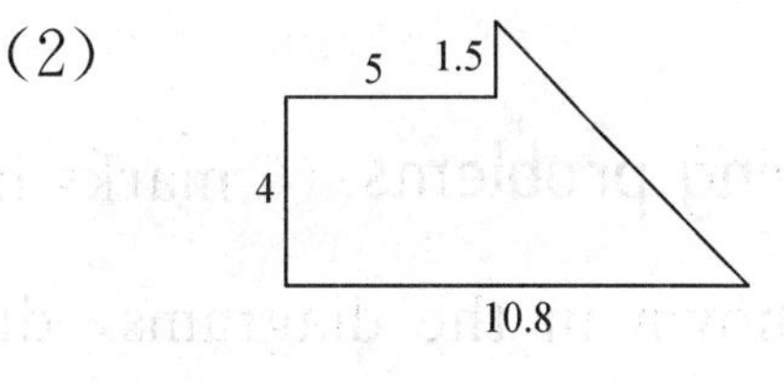

Diagram for Question 4(2)

Enhancement and extension

5 As shown in the diagram, in the rectangle $ABCD$, AD is 18 cm, and AB is 15 cm, E is the midpoint of BC and F is the midpoint of CD. Find the area of triangle AEF.

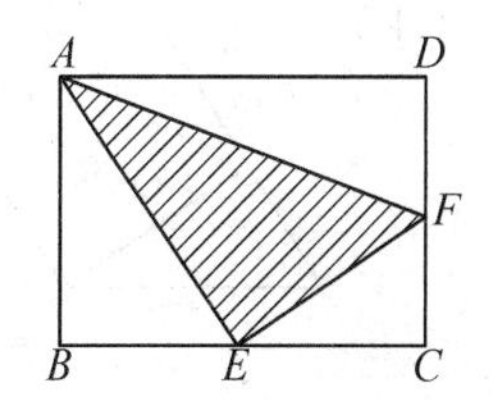

Diagram for Question 5

6 As shown in the diagram, in the right-angled trapezium $ABCD$, $AD = DC = 12$ cm, and the area of triangle ABE is 24 cm^2. Find the area of triangle BDF.

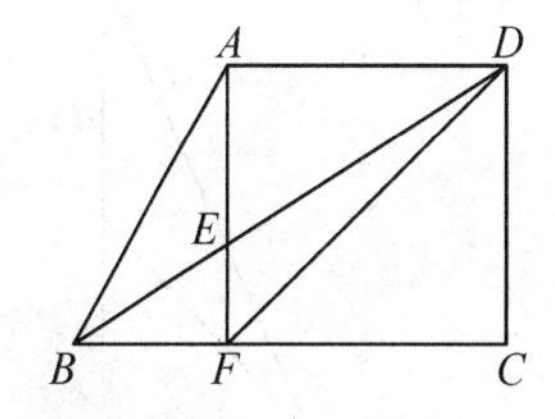

Diagram for Question 6

Unit test 5

A. Drawing problems. (6 marks in total)

❶ As shown in the diagrams, draw the height of each figure on the base indicated.

(1)

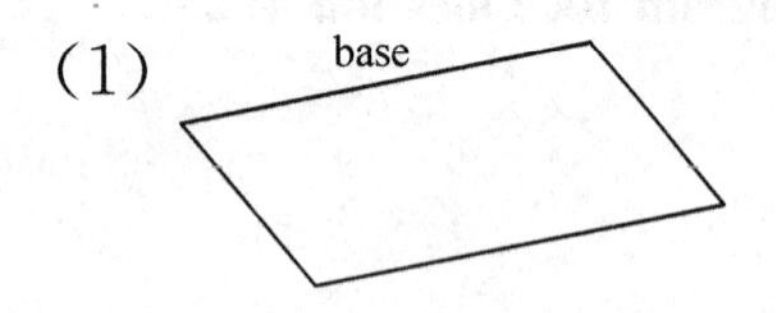

(2)

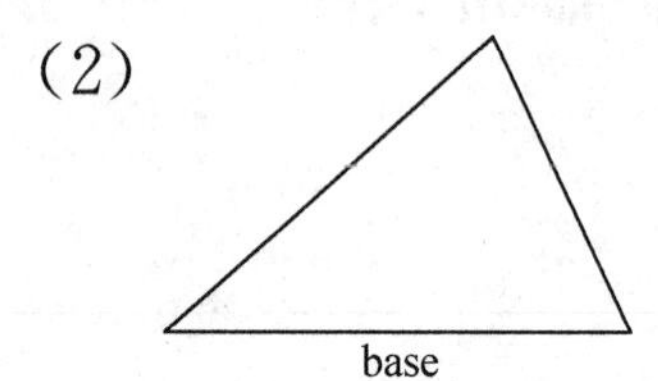

B. Calculation problems. (38 marks in total)

❷ As shown in the diagrams, find the area of each figure indicated below. (12 marks in total)

(1)

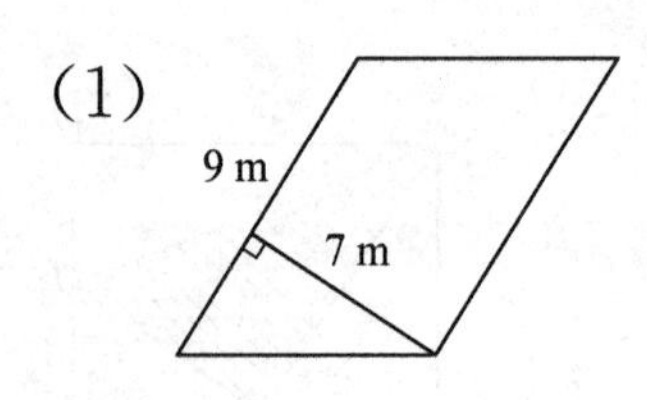

(2)

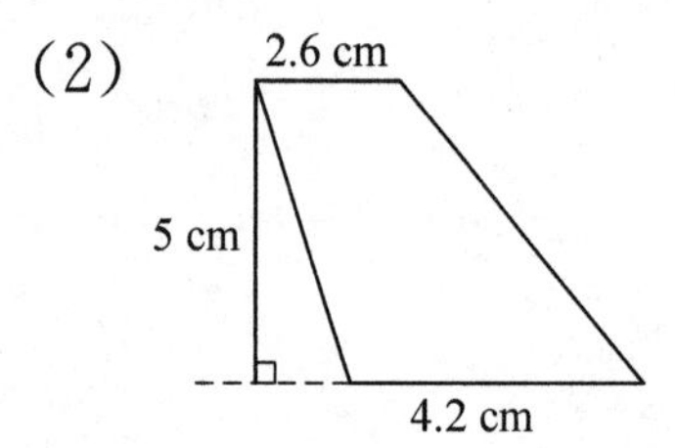

(3)

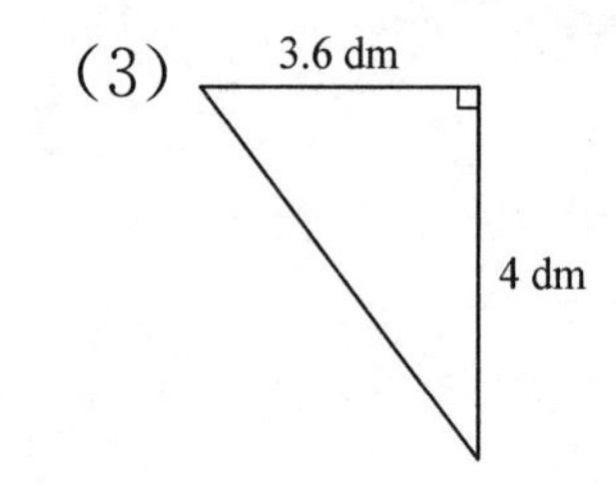

❸ As shown in the diagrams, find the unknown in each figure indicated below. (8 marks in total)

(1)

$S = 18\ m^2$, find a.

(2)

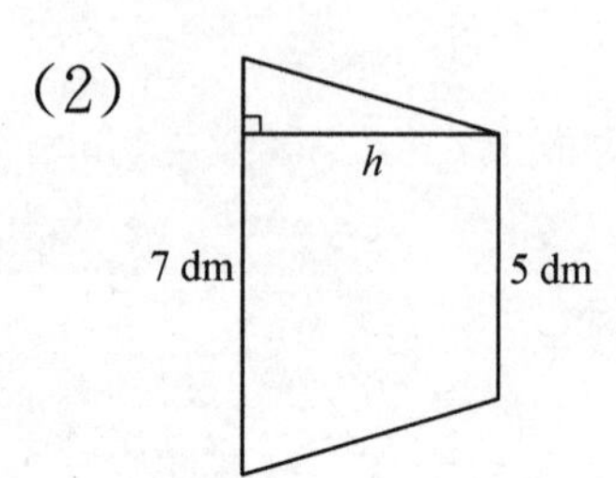

$S = 36\ dm^2$, find h.

4 As shown in the diagram, the perimeter of the parallelogram is 66 cm. Find the area. (6 marks in total)

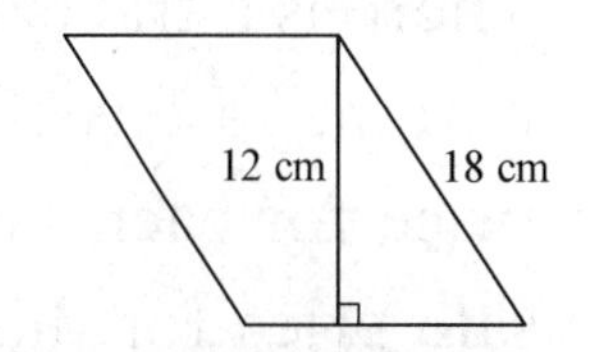

Diagram for Question 4

5 As shown in the diagram, given the area of the trapezium $ABCD$ is 64 cm^2, the top base is 6 cm, the bottom base is 10 cm, and the area of $\triangle AOD$ is 15 cm^2, find:

(1) the height of the trapezium; (3 marks in total)

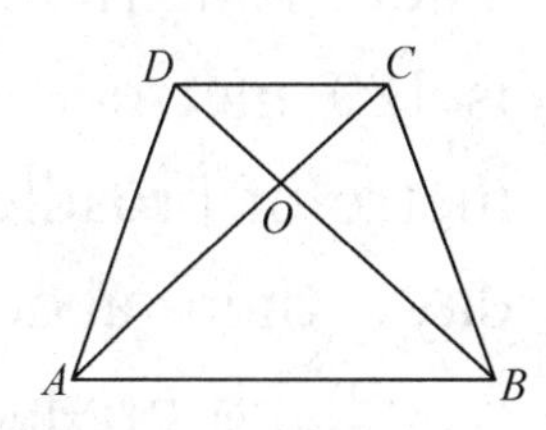

Diagram for Question 5

(2) the area of $\triangle AOB$. (3 marks in total)

6 As shown in the diagram, in rectangle $ABCD$, E is a point on the extended line AD beyond D, connect CE and BE. $AB = 15$ cm, $DE = 4$ cm, and the area of $\triangle DEF$ 12 cm^2. Find:

(1) the area of $\triangle CEF$; (3 marks in total)

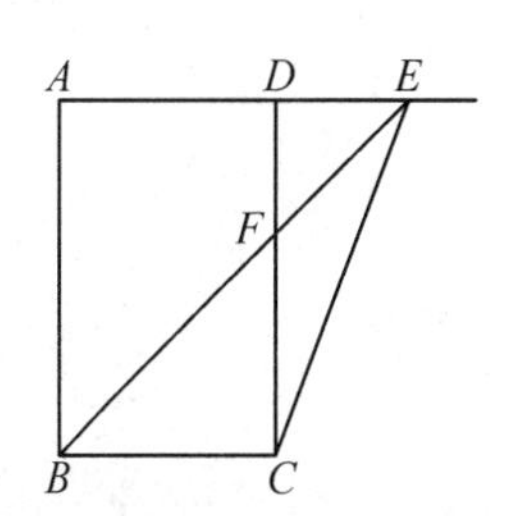

Diagram for Question 6

(2) the area of the trapezium $ABFD$. (3 marks in total)

C. Application problems. (36 marks in total)

7. There is a trapezium-shaped steel plate. The top base is 12 decimetres, the bottom base is 18 decimetres, and the height is 16 decimetres. If the sale price for each square metre of the steel plate is 50 yuan, how much is the sale price for this piece of steel plate?

8. There is a triangular piece of broadleaf woodland. The length of the base is 120 metres, exactly 3 times the length of its height. If each square metre of broadleaf woodland can produce about 75.8 grams of oxygen in a day, then about how many kilograms of oxygen can this broadleaf woodland produce in a day?

9. The area of a parallelogram is 1.5 times the area of a triangle. Given the base of the parallelogram is 36 cm, its height is 25 cm, and the base of the triangle is 32 cm, find the height of the triangle.

10. A rectangular piece of paper is 1 metre long and 9 decimetres wide. Right-angled triangles, each with the two sides of the right angle 6 centimetres and 5 centimetres long, are to be cut out from the paper. How many such triangles in total can be cut out from the paper?

11 There is a triangular signboard. The base is 1.6 metres and the height is 1.5 metres. If both faces of the signboard are to be painted, then 2.88 kilograms of paint is needed. How many kilograms of paint is needed to paint one square metre of the signboard?

12 One base of a parallelogram is 10 metres. If the base is reduced by 2 metres, then it becomes a trapezium with an area of 108 square metres. Find the area of the original parallelogram.

D. Concept problems. (20 marks in total)

(A) **True or false. (Put a "√" for true and a "×" for false)** (6 marks in total)

13 Generally a parallelogram does not have line symmetry. ( )

14 Two identical right-angled trapezia can definitely form a rectangle. ( )

15 If the areas of two triangles are equal, then their bases and heights are both equal. ( )

(B) **Multiple choice questions.** (6 marks in total)

16 When a triangle has an area of 24 cm^2, its base and height can be ( ).

(A) 5 cm and 4.8 cm (B) 3 cm and 16 mm
(C) 3.2 cm and 15 cm (D) 9 cm and 6 cm

17 If the top base, the bottom base, and the height of a trapezium are all enlarged to 3 times their original sizes, its area is enlarged to ( ) its original size.

(A) 3 times (B) 9 times (C) 18 times (D) 27 times

18 As shown in the diagram, the area of the trapezium is 4 times the area of the triangle, then the other base of the trapezium is ( ).

(A) 6 cm (B) 8 cm

(C) 9 cm (D) 15 cm

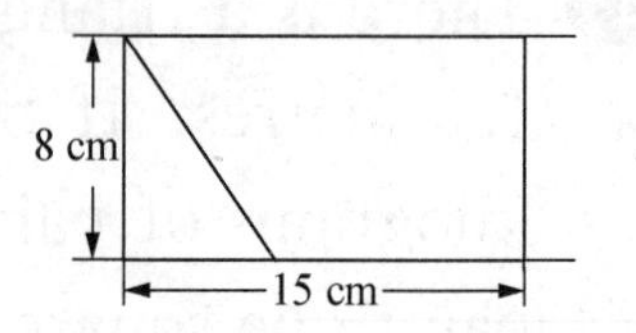

Diagram for Question 18

(C) **Fill in the brackets.** (8 marks in total)

19 From a rectangle 15 cm long and 12 cm wide, an obtuse-angled triangle of the largest possible area with base 9 cm is to be cut out. The area of the obtuse-angled triangle is ( ) cm^2.

20 A parallelogram has a base of 9.5 cm. If both bases, 9.5 cm long, are shortened by 2 cm and the height is unchanged, then the area is decreased by 8 cm^2. The area of the original parallelogram is ( ) cm^2.

21 The lengths of the three sides of a right-angled triangle are 6 cm, 8 cm and 10 cm. The height on the hypotenuse is ( ) cm.

22 As shown in the diagram, if the area of triangle A is 12 cm^2, then the area of triangle B is ( ) cm^2.

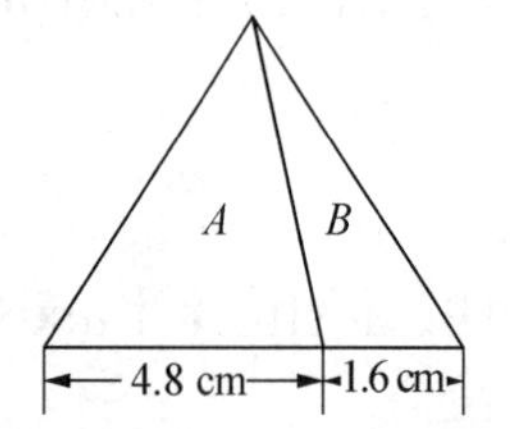

Diagram for Question 22

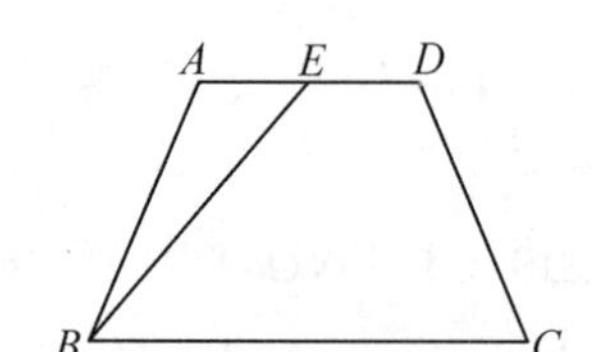

Diagram for Question 23

23 As shown in the diagram, the area of trapezium $ABCD$ is 18 dm^2, its height is 4 dm, BC is 5.4 dm and E is the midpoint of AD. The area of triangle ABE is ( ) dm^2.

24 Given that the product of the top base of a trapezium and its height is 5.4, and the product of the bottom base and its height is 8.8, then the area of the trapezium is ( ).

㉕ Two rectangular pieces of transparent tape with width 6 cm are used to form a parallelogram with four sides of equal length and a perimeter of 30 cm. The area of the parallelogram is (   ) cm^2.

㉖ Given in a right-angled trapezium, the base angle is 45°, the top base is 8 cm and the bottom base is 14 cm, then the area of the trapezium is (   ) cm^2.

Chapter 6 Consolidation and enhancement

6.1 Mixed four operations with decimals (1)

Basic questions

1 Work these out mentally and write down the answers.

(1) $2.7+7.2=$ (2) $7.1-2.9=$

(3) $5.25\times 0.4=$ (4) $4\div 2.5=$

(5) $10.6-0.6\times 1.5=$ (6) $1.4\div 0.8\times 1.2=$

2 Use the column method to calculate.

(1) 2.4×10.5

(2) 4.35×3.28
(Round to the nearest hundredth)

(3) $43.7\div 21$
(Round to the nearest tenth)

(4) $5.36\div 3.3$
(Express the result with a recurring decimal)

3 Work these out step by step. (Calculate smartly if possible)

(1) $7.25\div 2.5+(4.38-2.61)$

(2) $1.25\times 5.6\div 0.7$

(3) $(172.5-72.5)\times 0.12\div 0.01$

(4) $4.8\times 7.6+3.4\times 4.8-4.8$

4 Fill in the brackets.

(1) If $7.6 \times 2.37 = 18.012$, then $0.76 \times 2370 =$ (   ) and $180.12 \div 7.6 =$ (   ).

(2) $3.89 \times 2.4 = 38.9 \times$ (   ) $6.4 \times 0.125 = 6.4 \div$ (   )

$2.8 \times 3.4 =$ (   ) $\times 1.7$ $a \div 0.25 = a \times$ (   ) $(a > 0)$

(3) If $A \times 1.5 = B \times 1.1 = C \div 1 = D \div 0.9$ (A, B, C and D are greater than 0), then the greatest of the four numbers is (   ) and the least is (   ).

(4) If $54 \times 3.2 + 32 + 32 \times \square = 320$, then the number in the $\square$ is (   ).

5 True or false. (Put a "√" for true and a "×" for false)

(1) If $a > 0$, and $a \times 0.5 = b \div 0.5$, then a is 4 times b.   (   )

(2) When a decimal number with three decimal places is divided by a decimal number with one decimal place, the quotient must be a decimal number with two decimal places.   (   )

6 Multiple choice questions.

(1) When $a = 1.28 \times 0.25$, and $b = 1.28 \div 5$, comparing a and b, the result is (   ).

(A) $a > b$ (B) $a = b$ (C) $a < b$ (D) uncertain

(2) In decimal numbers with three decimal places that are rounded to 0.80, the difference between the greatest and the least is (   ).

(A) 0.004   (B) 0.005   (C) 0.009   (D) 0.01

Enhancement and extension

7 A truck travelled 18 kilometres in 0.6 hours. How many kilometres did the truck travel in one minute? How many minutes does it take the truck to travel 1 kilometre?

8 How many five-digit numbers can the five digits 1, 2, 3, 4 and 5 make up with no repetition? Putting all these numbers in order from the least to the greatest, what place is the number 24 135 in? If these five-digit numbers are put in order from the greatest to the least, what number is in the 50th place?

6.2 Mixed four operations with decimals (2)

Basic questions

1 Work these out mentally and write down the answers.

(1) $2 - 0.55 + 0.45 =$ (2) $14.4 - 4.4 \times 0.6 =$

(3) $0.4 + 0.6 \div 0.1 =$ (4) $1.8 \div 0.9 \times 1.8 =$

2 Work these out step by step.

(1) $21.45 - 2.45 \times 4.2 + 7.8$ (2) $(2.8 - 2.8 \times 0.56) \div (0.6 + 0.5)$

(3) $72 \times 0.75 - 36.36 \div 1.8$ (4) $5.5 \div 2.5 \times 0.5 \div (2.82 + 2.18)$

(5) $16.73 + 3.75 \div 7.5 \times 4.8$ (6) $(4.5 - 0.45) \div (0.1 + 0.2 \times 0.4)$

(7) $[7.85 + (3.9 - 3.51) \div 0.6] \times (6.3 + 0.73)$

(8) $7.2 \div [(3.6 \times 1.25 + 3.5) \times 0.25 - 1.28]$

3 Calculate in a simple and convenient way.

(1) $28.7-4.32-2.68$

(2) $82.6-(22.6+41.19)+1.19$

(3) $0.5\times1.25\times2.5\times6.4$

(4) $7.9\times12.5+1.25$

(5) $4\div12.5+4\div2.5$

(6) $4.8+4.8\times7.2-4.8\times6.95$

(7) $1.64+99\times4.5+2.86$

(8) $5.5\times7.8-2.5\times5.5+4.5\times5.3$

4 A factory is to process a batch of spare parts. It needs 25 people for 12 days to finish the job. If each worker processes 140 spare parts each day, how many spare parts are there in the batch? Now each worker is to process 10 more spare parts each day, and the task is required to be completed 2 days earlier, how many more workers are needed?

Enhancement and extension

5 When Number A is divided by Number B, the quotient is 4 and the remainder is 2. If Number A is increased to 3 times its original value and Number B is unchanged, then the quotient is 13 without a remainder. What is Number A originally?

6.3 Application of decimals — water, electricity and gas bills

Basic questions

1 Xiao Dingding's family uses a time-sharing electricity meter. Read their electricity bill statement carefully and find how much Xiao Dingding's family should pay for the month. (Round to the nearest tenth)

Meter reading this month	Amount used (kilowatt-hour)	Unit price (yuan)	Total amount (yuan)
5765	158	0.617	
3028	96	0.307	
Amount due this month (yuan)			

2 Read the water bill statement of Xiao Dingding's family carefully and solve the following questions.

Meter reading this month	Amount of water (cubic metre)	Unit price (yuan)	Total amount (yuan)
304	(Fresh water used)	1.63	83.13
	(Used water returned) to sewer	1.30	
Amount due this month (yuan)			

(1) How many cubic metres of fresh water was used?

(2) Regulation: Used water returned to sewer = fresh water used $\times 0.9$. How much did Xiao Dingding's family need to pay for the used water returned to sewer?

(3) How much did they need to pay for their water bill for the month?

3 The table below is the natural gas bill statement of Xiao Dingding's family over a certain period. Based on the figures in the table, please calculate how many cubic metres of gas was used and how much the family needed to pay for the period.

Previous metre reading	Metre reading this period	Amount of gas used (m^3)	Unit price (yuan/m^3)	Amount due (yuan)
348	412		2.50	

4 The terms and conditions by a local gas company say that if the amount of gas that a household uses is less than 1000 cubic metres in a year, it is charged 0.90 yuan per cubic metre; if it exceeds 1000 cubic metres, the exceeded amount is charged 1.50 yuan per cubic metre. The total amount of gas Xiao Ming's family used last year was 1120 cubic metres. How much did they pay for the gas last year?

5 The starting fare of a taxi in a region is 5 yuan (excluding the mileage travelled). The charge for each kilometre travelled is 1.2 yuan.

(1) One day Xiao Ming took a taxi and travelled 6 kilometres. How much did he need to pay?

(2) One day Xiao Hua took a taxi and paid 23 yuan. How many kilometres did Xiaohua travel by taxi?

Enhancement and extension

6 A class of 30 pupils took a group photo. The first 5 prints are charged at 3 yuan each. After this, for the extra prints, it is charged 0.9 yuan per print. If each pupil in the class wants one print of the group photo, how much did each pupil need to pay on average?

6.4 Writing equations to solve problems (4)

Basic questions

1. Solve the equations.

(1) $2.4x - 3.6 = 7.2$

(2) $0.4 + 5x = 2.4$

(3) $x + 5.8 - 2.5 = 9.4$

(4) $1.5(x - 0.3) = 4.8$

2. A new school term starts. Xiao Ya bought 4 notebooks in a stationery store with 50 yuan and got 6 yuan in change. How much did each notebook cost?

3. Before a school sports day, Teacher Ding went to a sports goods shop to buy long skipping ropes with 200 yuan. He wanted to buy 80 ropes, but he was short of 40 yuan. How much did each long skipping rope cost?

4. Xiao Dong went to buy buns with 20 yuan. He bought some pork floss buns with a unit price of 3.5 yuan and received 2.5 yuan in change. How many pork floss buns did he buy in total?

5 Mum bought 2 towels for 16.8 yuan in a supermarket. Based on this calculation, how much change should she get if she bought 5 such towels with 50 yuan?

6 The perimeter of a rectangle is 32 centimetres and its length is 9.5 centimetres. Find the width of the rectangle.

7 Xiao Ming had 30 yuan. He first bought a pack of beef jerkey. The change he got was exactly enough to buy 2 cartons of milk with a unit price of 6.8 yuan. How much did the pack of beef jerkey cost?

8 Teacher Wang bought some sports equipment for school. He bought 16 pairs of table tennis bats and 12 basketballs and paid 800 yuan in total. Each pair of table tennis bats cost 27.50 yuan. How much did each basketball cost?

9 Xiao Yong went to a stationery store with 68 yuan, exactly enough to buy 3 boxes of paints and 4 pens. If one pen cost 8 yuan, then how much did one box of paint cost?

10 Xiao Pang took out 40 sweets from each of 6 boxes all with the same number of sweets. The total number of the remaining sweets in the boxes is 90. How many sweets did each box have at first?

Enhancement and extension

11 A school bought 5 desks and 8 chairs at a total cost of 375 yuan. The unit price of a desk is 10 yuan more than the unit price of a chair. How much is the unit price of a chair?

6.5 Writing equations to solve problems (5)

Basic questions

1 Solve the equations.

(1) $2x + 7.1 = 3.2 \times 3$

(2) $8.4 - 1.6x = 1.2 \div 3$

(3) $(60 + x - 32) \div 4 = 12.5$

(4) $2.8x - 5.5 + 4.7x = 9.5$

2 A gas company currently has 1240 employees, 40 more than 6 times the number of employees 5 years ago. How many employees did the company have 5 years ago?

3 Peach trees and apricot trees are planted in an orchard. 370 of them are peach trees, 32 less than 3 times the number of apricot trees. How many apricot trees are planted in the orchard?

4 Teacher Zhang went to a shop with 350 yuan. He bought 4 footballs at the same price. The change he received was exactly enough to buy 5 basketballs with a unit price of 34 yuan. How much did each football cost?

5 Xiao Ya took 30 yuan to buy exercises books. He bought some exercise books with a unit price of 4.5 yuan and got 12 yuan in change. How many exercises books did he buy in total?

6 If the length of a rectangle is unchanged while the width is increased by 4 centimetres, it will become a square with perimeter 58 centimetres. Find the width of the rectangle.

7 Factory A has 248 tonnes of steel and Factory B has 112 tonnes. If Factory A uses 18 tonnes of steel each day, then after how many days will the amount of the remaining steel in Factory A be 26 tonnes less than the amount Factory B has?

8 There are two numbers A and B. If the sum of Number A multiplied by 3 and Number B divided by 2 is 95, and Number A is 24, then what is Number B?

9. Xiao Qiao took 15 yuan to buy 4 pencils and 7 exercise books and got 0.6 yuan in change. Given the unit price of an exercise book is 1.6 yuan, find the unit price of a pencil.

10. Mr Li planned to make 1 set of spare part A, 2 sets of spare part B and 5 sets of spare part C in 18 hours. Given it took him 3 hours to make 1 set of spare part A and 4 hours to make 1 set of spare part B, how many hours would it take him to make 1 set of spare part C?

Enhancement and extension

11. A school bought 72 sets of desks and chairs (1 set consists of 1 desk and 1 chair) at a total cost of 7920 yuan. The price of a desk was 5 yuan more than the price of two chairs. How much did one chair cost?

6.6 Areas of figures (1)

Basic questions

1. Draw a (the) height corresponding to the base indicated in the triangle and parallelogram.

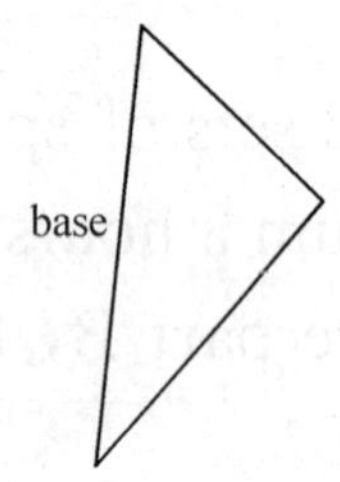

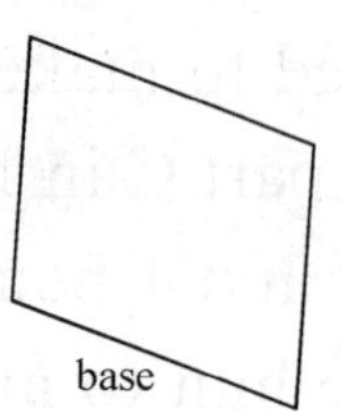

2. Calculate the area of each figure below. (unit: cm)

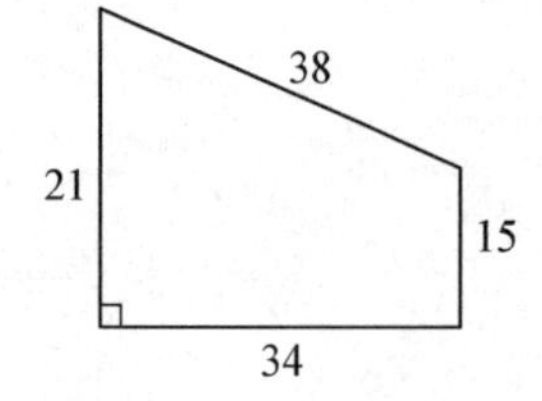

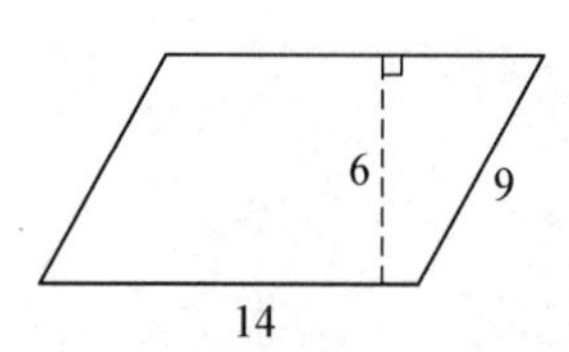

3. The area of a trapezium is 29.64 square centimetres. The top base is 4.6 centimetres, 2.2 centimetres shorter than the bottm base. Find the height of the trapezium.

4. Find the area of the shaded part in the figure. (unit: cm)

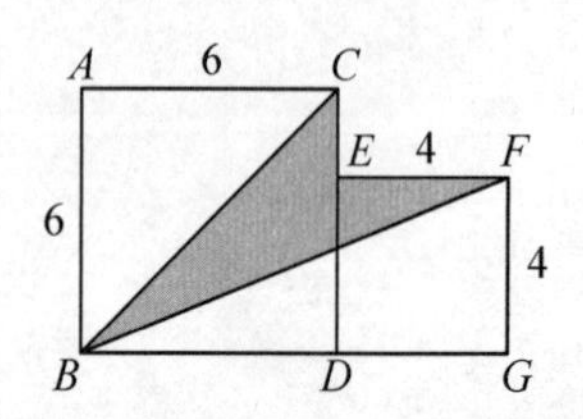

Diagram for Question 4

5 In the right-angled triangle ABC, $BEDF$ is a rectangle, $BE = 8$ cm, $BF = 5$ cm, $BE = 2AE$, and $CF = 2BF$.

(1) Is the area of triangle BCD equal to the area of trapezium $CDEF$?

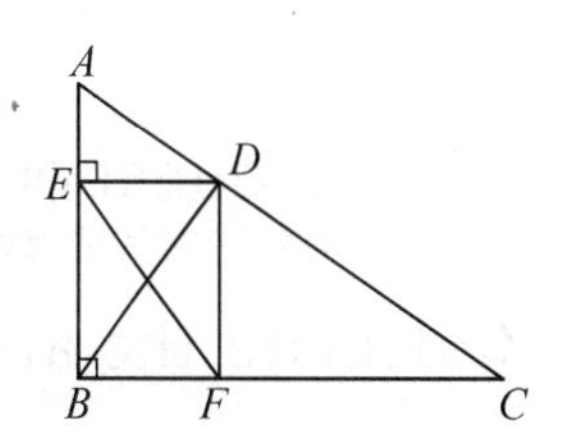

Diagram for Question 5

(2) How many times the area of triangle ADE is the area of triangle ABC?

6 As shown in the diagram, the side length of square $ABCD$ is 9 cm, and the side length of square $DEFH$ is 6 cm.

(1) What is the area of trapezium $ABCH$?

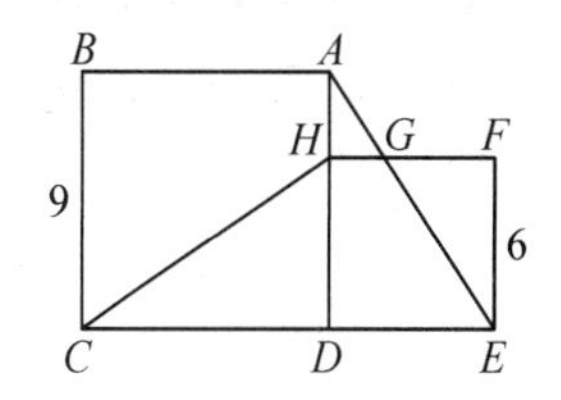

Diagram for Question 6

(2) How many square centimetres larger than the area of triangle AHG is the area of triangle EFG?

Enhancement and extension

7 As shown in the diagram, in the parallelogram $ABCD$, E and F are points of trisection of AC and BC, respectively. The area of the parallelogram is 54 square centimetres. Find the area of the shaded part.

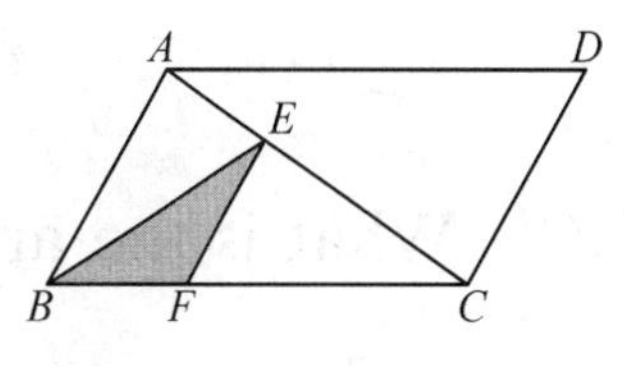

Diagram for Question 7

6.7 Areas of figures (2)

Basic questions

1. Calculate the area of the figure below. (unit: cm)

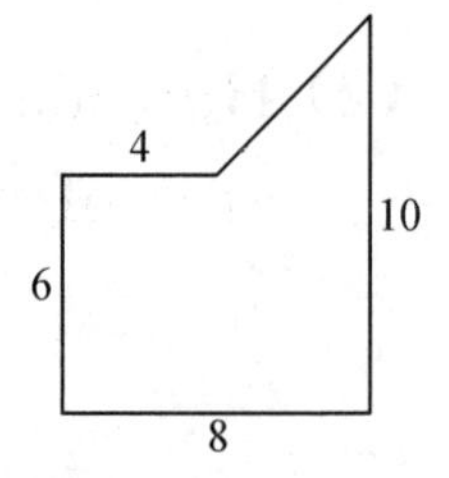

Diagram for Question 1

2. As shown in the diagram, the side length of the square $ABCD$ is 20 cm, $AE = 5$ cm and $AF = 4$ cm. Find the area of triangle CEF.

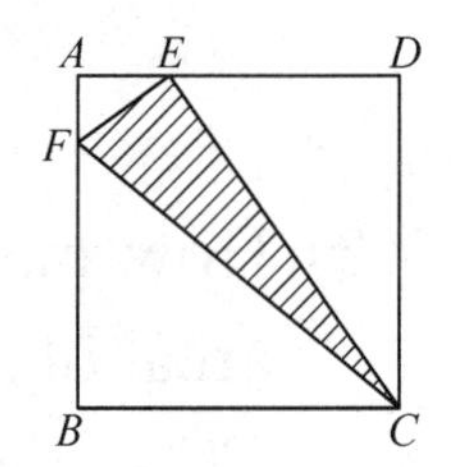

Diagram for Question 2

3. Two right-angled isosceles set squares with different sizes are put together so that they overlap as shown in the diagram, $BC = 10$ cm and $CE = 6$ cm. Questions:

(1) What is the area of triangle CDE?

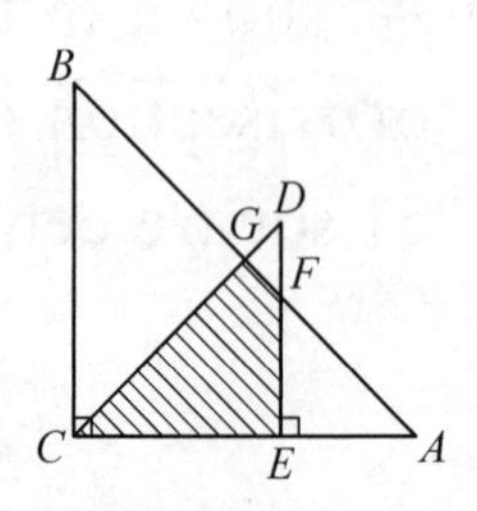

(2) What is the area of trapezium $BCEF$?

Diagram for Question 3

(3) What is the area of triangle BCG?

(4) What is the area of the overlapped part (i.e., the shaded part)?

4 The perimeter of the square $ABCD$ is 24 cm. $CEGF$ is a rectangle, $EC = 2BE$ and $DF = 2FC$. Find the area of the shaded part.

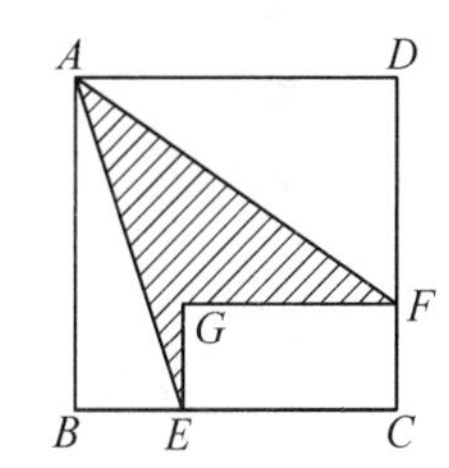

Diagram for Question 4

5 As shown in the diagram, the right-angled trapezium $ABCD$, whose area is 90 cm^2, is divided into two triangles, M and N, so that the area of Triangle N is 1.5 times the area of Triangle M.

(1) What is the area of Triangle M?

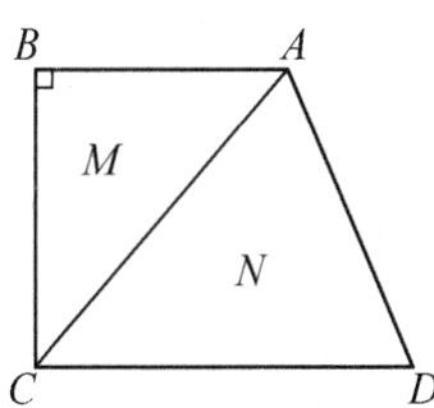

Diagram for Question 5

(2) If $AB = 8$ cm, then what are the lengths of the height and the bottom base of the trapezium?

Enhancement and extension

6 As shown in the diagram, the area of the triangle ABO is 9 square centimetres. The length of the line segment BO is 3 times the length of OD. The diagonals of the trapezium, AC and BD, intersect at O. Question: How many square centimetres is the area of trapezium $ABCD$?

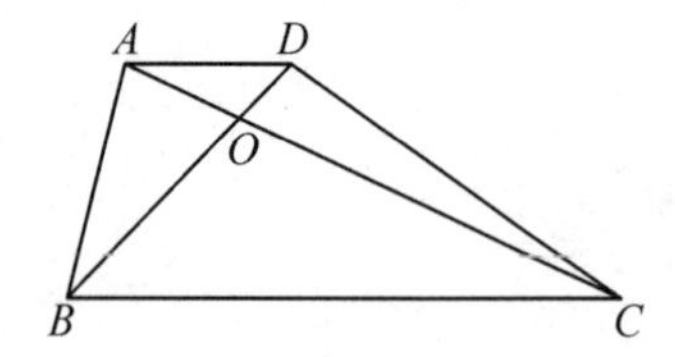

Diagram for Question 6

6.8 Mathematics plaza — calculation of time

Basic questions

1 Calculate.

(1) 36 minutes −13 minutes 30 seconds= ________

(2) 5 hours 28 minutes+3 hours 32 minutes= ________

(3) 9 minutes 14 seconds −5 minutes 48 seconds +1 minute 25 seconds= ________

2 Xiao Pang arrived at a youth activities centre at 10:45 in the morning, and spent 48 minutes there taking part in activities. At what time did Xiao Pang leave the youth activities centre?

3 It takes 45 minutes from the Xinzhuang Station to the Shanghai Train Station by metro. If a train reaches the Shanghai Train Station at 9:35 in the morning, at what time did the train leave the Xinzhuang Station?

4 Xiao Ya arrives at school at 8:05 each morning. She has 4 lessons, each lasting 35 minutes. There are in total 20 minutes for the morning exercise routine and eye exercise, and 50 minutes of breaks between lessons for recess and activities. At what time does Xiao Ya leave school for home in the morning?

5 It took Xiao Ya 1 hour and 50 minutes to walk up to the top of a hill. After taking a rest for 23 minutes, she walked back and it took her 1 hour and 26 minutes to reach the foot of the hill. How much time did it take Xiao Ya in total from the beginning of walking up until she arrived at the foot of the hill?

6 It takes 13 minutes to bake a loaf of bread in an oven. If a loaf of bread has been baked for 6 minutes and 32 seconds, how much time does it still need to bake?

7 Xiao Qiao does reading from 18:30 to 20:20 every day and then how much time does she spend on reading in a week (7 days) in total?

8 Xiao Pang is going to a concert, and it takes him 45 minutes to get there and 40 minutes to get back home. The concert is from 19:30 to 21:30. Can you help Xiao Pang calculate at what time he should leave for the concert and at what time he will get back home?

Enhancement and extension

9 A film lasts 95 minutes. A cinema plans to start the film at 9 o'clock in the morning. The interval between two shows is 20 minutes for the films shown before 16:00 and 15 minutes for those after 16:00. According to the information, answer the following questions.

(1) The cinema closes at 22:00. Can you work out at what time the last film should end?

(2) The ticket prices of a show vary depending on the showtime. Each ticket is 50 yuan for the shows before 16:00 and 80 yuan for those after 16:00. The cinema has a total of 600 seats and on average there are 100 seats unsold for each show. If a film is on show for one week (7 days), how much money does the cinema earn by selling the tickets?

6.9 Mathematics plaza — coding

Basic questions

1. Fill in the spaces.
   (1) A postcode consists of (　　　) digits.
   (2) A landline phone number in the city area of Shanghai consists of (　　　) digits.
   (3) A second-generation identification card number consists of (　　　) digits.

2. Please tell the meanings that different digits on the identification card "310229197711170418" represent.
   The 1st and 2nd digits represent the (　　　　　　　　).
   The 3rd and 4th digits represent the (　　　　　　　　).
   The 5th and 6th digits represent the (　　　　　　　　).
   The 7th — 14th digits represent the (　　　　　　　　).
   The 15th and 16th digits represent the (　　　　　　　　).
   The 17th digit represents the (　　　　　　).
   The 18th digit represents the (　　　　　　).

3. Use the knowledge you have learned and draw lines to match.

31010719390519××57	Xiao Ming
31010719650324××34	Xiao Ming's father
31010719421208××68	Xiao Ming's aunt in Beijing
31010719950207××54	Xiao Ming's grandpa
11010519690820××62	Xiao Ming's grandma

4. Tell the birth date and the gender of each person according to their identification cards.
   Xiao Zhang: 310229198411170418 date of birth (　　　　　), gender (　　)
   Xiao Wang: 110105200412010883 date of birth (　　　　　), gender (　　)
   Xiao Liu: 310101196905173410 date of birth (　　　　　), gender (　　)

Xiaojun: 34011519920805158X date of birth (   ), gender (   )

5 When making a long distance call, one needs to dial the area code first. Find each of the area codes of the following cities.

Shanghai: Beijing: Nanjing:

Chongqing: Tianjing: Shenzhen:

6 Multiple choice question.

The numbers on the identification cards of Person A and Person B are as follows: 31010219680806××14 and 31010719860704××28. The correct description of the following is (   ).

(A) They are both females. Person A is 18 years older than Person B.

(B) They are a male and a female. Person B is 18 years older than Person A.

(C) They are a male and a female. Person A is 18 years older than Person B.

(D) They are both males. Person B is 18 years older than Person A.

Enhancement and extension

7 Do a survey about the postcode of the primary school that you are in. What does each digit in the postcode stand for?

8 In your daily life, what kinds of number coding have you come across? Please give an explanation.

Unit test 6

A. Calculation problems. (40 marks in total)

1 Work these out mentally and write down the answers. (4 marks in total)

(1) $1 \div 0.25 \times 8 =$

(2) $8.7 \times 0.5 \times 20 =$

(3) $7.6 - 1.6 \times 0.4 =$

(4) $1 \div (5.4 + 7.1) =$

2 Use the column method to calculate. (6 marks in total)

(1) $7.24 \times 5.8 \approx$ (keep the result to two decimal places)

(2) $2.3 \div 11 =$ (Express the quotient with a recurring decimal)

3 Solve the equations. (6 marks in total)

(1) $0.6x - 4.9 = 2.6$

(2) $1.6(x + 4.5) = 4.8 \times 2$

4 Work these out step by step. (Calculate smartly if possible) (24 marks in total)

(1) $5.8 - 0.8 \div (1.5 + 0.5)$

(2) $26.22 - 58.4 - 41.6 + 73.78$

(3) $1.25 \times 1.6 \times 0.25$

(4) $(3.6 \times 1.2 + 1.6 \times 3.6) \div 0.28$

(5) $2.25 \div (7.5 \div 2.5 + 1.5)$ (6) $5.6 \times [0.4 + (10.04 - 9.59) \div 0.5]$

B. Application problems. (30 marks in total)

5. A school canteen received a batch of coal. If it uses 30 kilograms of the coal each day, it could last 40 days. Due to the improvement of the stoves, it saves 5 tonnes of coals each day. How many days can the batch of coal actually last?

6. Xiao Dingding bought 4 egg tarts at a fast food restaurant with 30 yuan. The change he got was exactly enough to buy 2 pairs of Orlean grilled chicken wings with a unit price of 7 yuan. How much did 1 egg tart cost?

7. A school planned to buy 2 sets of office desks with a unit price of 480 yuan. Later, it decided to use the money to buy 7 chairs instead of the office desks. The money was then not enough and the school paid another 90 yuan. What was the unit price of a chair?

8 A school bought 16 pairs of badminton rackets at a total cost of 800 yuan. The price for each pair of badminton racket is 2 yuan more than 8 times the price for a skipping rope. What is the price for a skipping rope?

9 The starting fare of a taxi in a city is 10 yuan (for a maximum of 3 kilometres). When it travels more than 3 kilometres, each additional kilometre travelled is charged 2 yuan. When it travels over 10 kilometres, each additional kilometre is charged 3 yuan.

(1) Xiao Ming took a taxi and travelled 8 kilometres, how much did he need to pay?

(2) Xiao Hua once took a taxi and paid 30 yuan. How many kilometres did he travel in the taxi?

C. Figure problems. (12 marks in total)

10 Find the area of the composite figure. (unit: m)

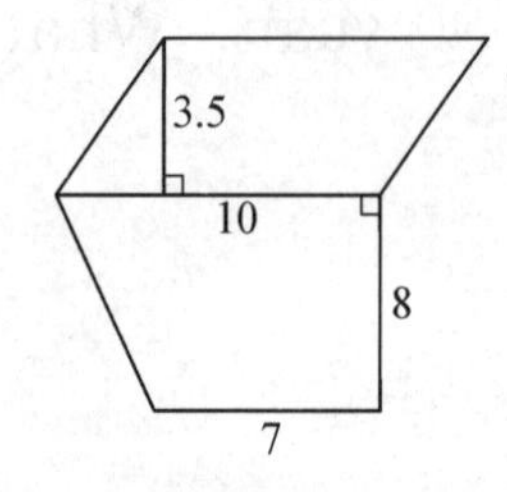

Diagram for Question 10

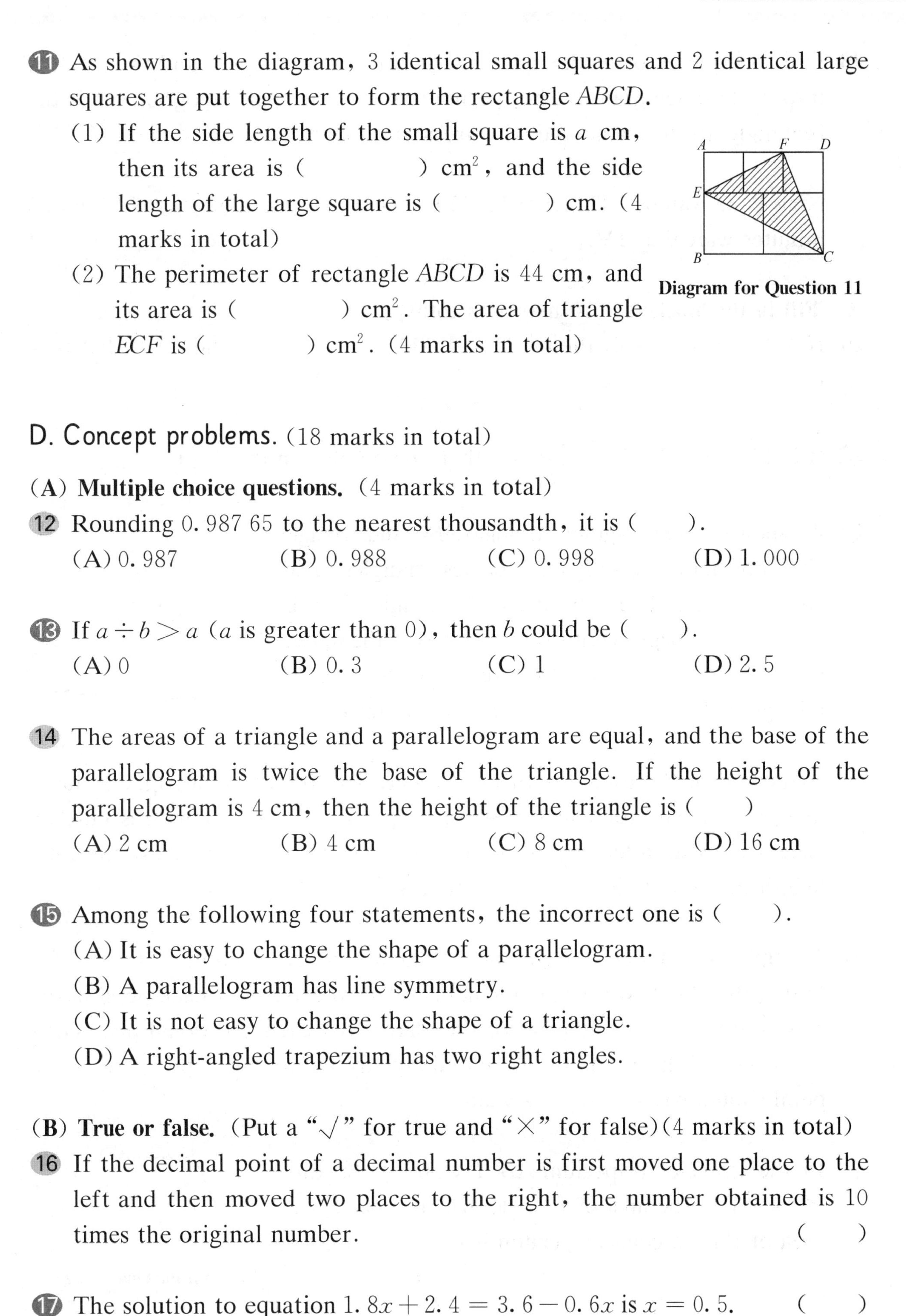

11 As shown in the diagram, 3 identical small squares and 2 identical large squares are put together to form the rectangle $ABCD$.

(1) If the side length of the small square is a cm, then its area is (　　　　　) cm^2, and the side length of the large square is (　　　　　) cm. (4 marks in total)

(2) The perimeter of rectangle $ABCD$ is 44 cm, and its area is (　　　　　) cm^2. The area of triangle ECF is (　　　　　) cm^2. (4 marks in total)

Diagram for Question 11

D. Concept problems. (18 marks in total)

(A) Multiple choice questions. (4 marks in total)

12 Rounding 0.987 65 to the nearest thousandth, it is (　　).

(A) 0.987　　(B) 0.988　　(C) 0.998　　(D) 1.000

13 If $a \div b > a$ (a is greater than 0), then b could be (　　).

(A) 0　　(B) 0.3　　(C) 1　　(D) 2.5

14 The areas of a triangle and a parallelogram are equal, and the base of the parallelogram is twice the base of the triangle. If the height of the parallelogram is 4 cm, then the height of the triangle is (　　)

(A) 2 cm　　(B) 4 cm　　(C) 8 cm　　(D) 16 cm

15 Among the following four statements, the incorrect one is (　　).

(A) It is easy to change the shape of a parallelogram.

(B) A parallelogram has line symmetry.

(C) It is not easy to change the shape of a triangle.

(D) A right-angled trapezium has two right angles.

(B) True or false. (Put a "√" for true and "×" for false) (4 marks in total)

16 If the decimal point of a decimal number is first moved one place to the left and then moved two places to the right, the number obtained is 10 times the original number. (　　)

17 The solution to equation $1.8x + 2.4 = 3.6 - 0.6x$ is $x = 0.5$. (　　)

18 Use four pieces of wooden stripes to make a rectangle, and then pull it into a parallelogram. The perimeters of the parallelogram and the rectangle are the same, but the areas are different. (   )

19 Xiao Pang watched TV from 19:55 to 21:05. He spent a total of 1 hour 50 minutes watching TV. (   )

(C) **Fill in the brackets.** (10 marks in total)

20 If $6.48 \div 1.8 = 3.6$, then $0.18 \times 0.036 =$ (   ) and $0.648 \div 360 =$ (   ).

21 If $5.4 \times 3.6 + 0.36 \times \square = 36$, then the number in the $\square$ is (   ).

22 As shown in the diagram, triangle ABC and triangle CDE are both right-angled isosceles triangles, and $DE = 12$ cm. Then the area of triangle CDE is (   ) square centimetres, the area of the square is (   ) square centimetres, and the area of triangle ABC is (   ) square centimetres.

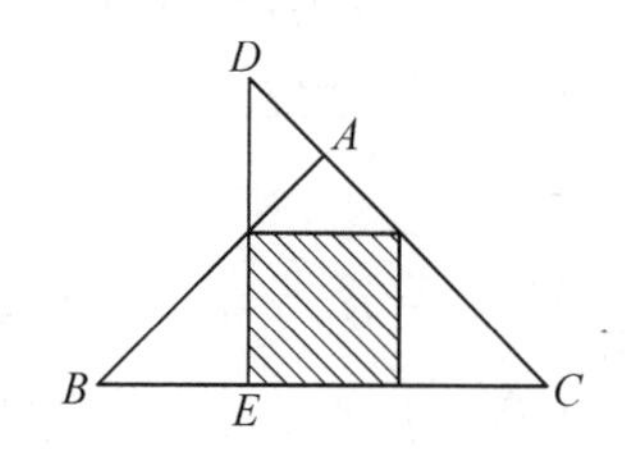

Diagram for Question 22

23 After half of the total length plus m metres were cut off a rope, it had 2 metres left. The total length of the rope is (   ) metres (use an expression with a letter to represent it); when $m = 5.5$ metres, the total length of the rope is (   ) metres.

24 40 pupils in Class 5(1) are going to take a graduation photo. The cost for taking the photo is 30 yuan, including 4 free prints. Now each pupil in the class wants to have one print of the photo, but each additional print costs 1.5 yuan. If the total cost is shared equally by all the pupils, then each pupil should pay (   ) yuan.

25 In the isosceles trapezium $ABCD$, $AE \perp BC$ and $BC = 2AD$. The area of triangle ABE is 1 cm^2. The area of the isosceles trapezium is (   ) cm^2.

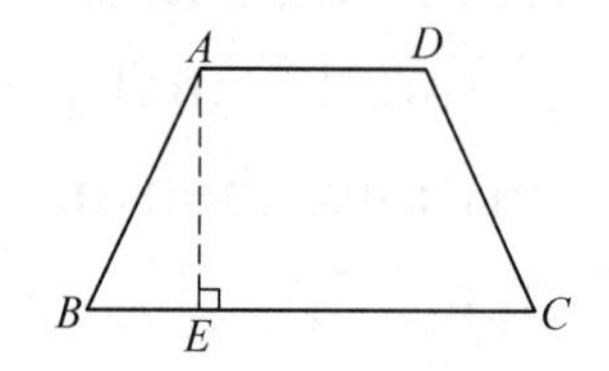

Diagram for Question 25

Mid-term test

A. Calculation problems. (42 marks in total)

1 Work these out mentally and write down the answers. (6 marks in total)

(1) $0.3 \div 0.01 =$

(2) $1.2 \times 0.4 =$

(3) $9.6 - 3.8 - 4.6 =$

(4) $0.28 + 7.2 =$

(5) $0.9 \div 4.5 \times 0.2 =$

(6) $0.125 \times 0.7 \times 0.8 =$

2 Use the column method to calculate. (Check the answer to the question marked with *) (12 marks in total)

(1) $12.5 \times 0.82 =$

(2) $0.47 \times 0.28 \approx$
(Round to the nearest tenth)

(3) $4.8 \div 0.43 \approx$
(Round to the nearest hundredth)

* (4) $1.296 \div 0.18 =$

3 Work these out step by step. (Calculate smartly if possible) (16 marks in total)

(1) $(7 - 2.68) \div 4.8$

(2) $(0.25 + 1.7) \times 4$

(3) $5.4 \times 6.8 + 5.4 \times 4.2 - 5.4$

(4) $8.58 - 8.58 \div 3.3 \times 2.5$

4 Write mixed number sentences and calculate. (8 marks in total)

(1) 1. 2 multiplied by 1. 2 is added to half of 2. 2. What is the sum?

(2) The sum of 2. 7 and 1. 9 is divided by the difference of 10. 8 minus 1. 6. What is the quotient?

B. Application problems. (36 marks in total. 5 marks each for Questions 5 - 10; 6 marks for Question 11)

5 A bottle can be filled with 0. 55 litres of sports drink. How many bottles can 100 litres of sports drink fill? How many litres will be left over?

6 The weight of a chicken egg is 0. 061 kilogram. The weight of an ostrich egg is 0. 025 kilograms more than 25 times the weight of a chicken egg. What is the weight of an ostrich egg?

7 8 sleepers are used to pave a 3-metre-long rail track. Based on this calculation, to pave a 1. 8-kilometre-long rail track, how many sleepers are needed?

8 A road maintenance team needed to repair a road. It planned to complete it in 45 days. In fact, the team repaired 1.2 kilometres of the road each day, so the task was completed 3 days earlier. How many kilometres were to be repaired each day originally in the plan?

9 The average weight of the 18 boys in Class 5(1) is 36 kilograms and the average weight of the 12 girls is 34 kilograms. What is the average weight of the pupils in the class?

10 In a supermarket, a 1.25 litre bottle of coke costs 4.5 yuan. Now the supermarket launches a sales promotion in two specific ways: the first is buying one box (6 bottles) at 20 yuan; the second is buying three and getting one free. If Xiao Pang wants to buy 16 bottles of coke, what is the least amount Xiao Pang has to pay?

11 A school is having an event and the campus needs to be decorated with flowers. A flower shop happens to have a promotion: one bunch of carnations consisting of 20 stalks is priced at 30 yuan, and one bunch of roses consisting of 15 stalks is priced at 40 yuan. Both are sold in bunches only. The school plans to buy both types of flowers for a total of 200 stalks. Please provide some purchase plans and calculate the total price for

each plan.

	Carnation (bunch)	Rose (bunch)
Plan One		
Plan Two		
Plan Three		

C. Concept problems. (22 marks in total)

(A) **Fill in the brackets.** (12 marks in total)

12 4 kg 36 g=(　　　　) kg　　　　$0.56\ m^2$=(　　　　) dm^2

13 Fill in the ○ with ">" or "<".

$3.05 \div 0.9$ ○ 3.05×0.9　　　　$0.4\dot{3}$ ○ $0.\dot{4}\dot{3}$

14 If 9.954 is rounded to the nearest hundredth, it is (　　　　), and to one decimal place, it is (　　　　).

15 After 2.5 is repeatedly subtracted from 89.5 (　　　　) times, it has a remainder of 4.5.

16 When multiplying Number A and Number B, if Number A is increased by 1.6 and Number B is unchanged, the product is increased by 7.2. If Number B is decreased by 2.9 and Number A is unchanged, the product is decreased by 11.02. The product of Number A and Number B is (　　　　).

17 The head of a shark is 2.4 metres long. The length of the body is equal to the length of its head plus the length of its tail. The length of its tail is 1.5 times the length of its head. The total length of this shark is (　　　　) metres.

18 Car parking rates in the car park of the Shanghai Pudong International Airport are as follows:

Long stay: 70 yuan per day. Short stay: 10 yuan per hour for first 2 hours; 15 yuan per hour thereafter.

Xiao Pang's dad paid 50 yuan. He parked for (   ) hours.

19 The whole number parts of two decimal numbers each with one decimal place are both 7. After the two numbers are multiplied and rounded to one decimal place, it is about 60.0. The exact product is (   ).

20 Three people, Person A, Person B, and Person C, bought 8 buns in total and shared them equally. Person A paid the cost for 5 buns, Person B paid the cost for 3 buns, and Person C did not have money with him. After the buns were eaten, they calculated and found that Person C should give 6.4 yuan to Person A and Person B. Person A should get (   ) yuan back.

(B) True or false. (5 marks in total)

21 If two zeros are added at the end of 0.9, the number is increased by 100 times. (   )

22 $0.050\,150\,1\cdots \approx 0.0\dot{5}0\dot{1}$. (   )

23 $8.3 \times 6.2 + 0.83 \times 38 = 0.83 \times (6.2 + 3.8)$ (   )

24 The product of two pure decimal numbers must be less than their sum. (   )

25 The product of Number A and Number B is 1.5 times Number A and 1.2 times Number B. The product of Number A and Number B is 1.8. (   )

(C) Multiple choice questions. (5 marks in total)

26 In the four numbers 0.303, $0.30\dot{3}$, $0.3\dot{0}\dot{3}$ and $0.\dot{3}0\dot{3}$, there is/are (   ) number(s) greater than $0.3\dot{0}\dot{3}$.

(A) one (B) two (C) three (D) none

27 In the following equations, the one that leads to $a < 1$ is ( ).
(A) $6.3 \div a = 1$ (B) $a \times 0.3 = 1$ (C) $a \div 0.1 = 1$ (D) $0.8 \times a = 1$

28 ( ) has the same product as 10.6×1.74.
(A) 1.06×1.74 (B) 1.06×174
(C) 0.106×1740 (D) 1060×0.0174

29 When a number is rounded, it is about 5.70. The range of the number is ( ).
(A) greater than or equal to 5.69 but less than 5.74
(B) greater than or equal to 5.695 but less than 5.704
(C) greater than or equal to 5.70 but less than 5.74
(D) greater than or equal to 5.695 but less than 5.705

30 Xiao Pang took three mid-term tests in Chinese, mathematics and English. His score in mathematics is 2 marks higher than his mean score of the three tests. His score in English is 5 marks higher than in Chinese. In the three subjects, his score in ( ) is the highest.
(A) mathematics (B) English
(C) Chinese (D) uncertain

End of term test

A. Calculation. (44 marks in total)

1 Work these out mentally and write down the answers. (6 marks in total)

(1) $1.8 \times 0.5 \times 0.2 =$

(2) $0.6 \times 3 \div 0.6 \times 3 =$

(3) $1.6 \div 1.25 \div 0.08 =$

(4) $1.2 - 0.2 \times 0.8 =$

(5) $0.206 \times 0.95 \approx$
(Keep the result to two decimal places)

(6) $0.76 \div 0.24 =$
(Express the quotient with a recurring decimal)

2 Solve the equations. (12 marks in total)

(1) $2 \div x = 5$

(2) $48x - 70 = 50$

(3) $3(x + 3.5) = 13.5$

(4) $38x - (16 + 13x) = 24$

3 Work these out step by step. (Calculate smartly if possible) (18 marks in total)

(1) $58.475 + 9.89 - 8.475 + 10.11$

(2) $76.48 + 96 \div 2.4 \times 3$

(3) $12.9 \times 2.8 + 12.9 + 6.2 \times 12.9$

(4) $31.32 \div (0.4 \times 0.9) \div 0.1$

(5) $2.5 \times 1.25 \times 0.48$

(6) $[0.75 \div (1 - 0.75) + 0.3] \times 1.8$

4 Write mixed number sentences and calculate. (8 marks in total)

(1) Subtracting 5.1 from 4 times a number is equal to multiplying 3.5 by 0.6. What is the number? (Use an equation to solve)

(2) 14.85 is divided by the product of the sum of 8.7 and 1.3 multiplied by 2.5. What is the quotient?

B. Application problems.

(36 marks in total. 5 marks each for Questions 5 - 10; 6 marks for Question 11)

5 Xiao Ming walked along a 50-metre-long straight path four times. It took 76 steps the first time, 78 steps the second time, 80 steps the third time, and 78 steps the fourth time. About how many metres is the average length of Xiao Ming's steps? (Keep the result to two decimal places)

6 Hua Feng Software Company was making a batch of software. It planned to make 120 pieces each day and finish the task in 30 days. In fact, the task was finished 5 days earlier than planned due to improved efficiency. How many more pieces than planned were actually made each day?

7 There are 200 peach trees and pear trees altogether in an orchard. The number of peach trees is 10 less than twice the number of pear trees. How many pear trees and peach trees are there in the orchard? (Use an equation to solve)

8 The shape of a decorative board at the entrance of a self-service shop is an isosceles trapezium. The top base is 16 metres long, the bottom base is 22 metres long, and the height is 3 metres long. About 0.5 kilograms of paint is needed to cover each square metre of the board. Question: How many kilograms of paint is needed to cover both sides of the board?

9 The table below shows the electricity bill of Xiao Ya's family in November.

Previous month's reading	This month's reading	Consumption ratio	Amount of electricity used (kilowatt-hour)	Unit price (yuan)	Total price (yuan)
7389 2552	7539 2690	1 1		0.6170 0.3070	

Question: How much should Xiao Ya's family pay for the November electricity bill?

10 As shown in the diagram, the perimeter of the square is 32 cm, and A is the midpoint of the side of the square. Find the area of trapezium $ABCD$.

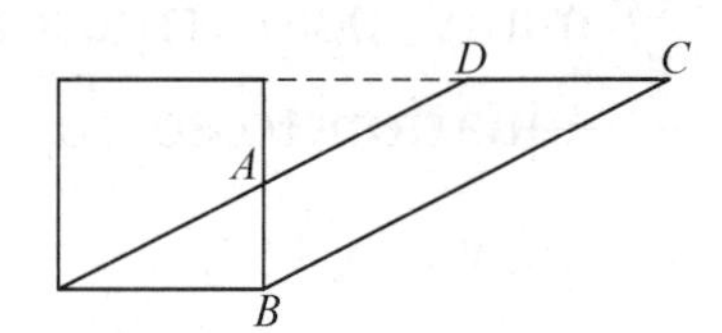

Diagram for Question 10

11 As shown in the diagram, AE divides the parallelogram $ABCD$ into triangle ABE and trapezium $AECD$, and the area of the trapezium is $24\ \text{cm}^2$ greater than the area of the triangle. Given $BE = 11$ cm and $EC = 4$ cm, what is the area of the parallelogram $ABCD$?

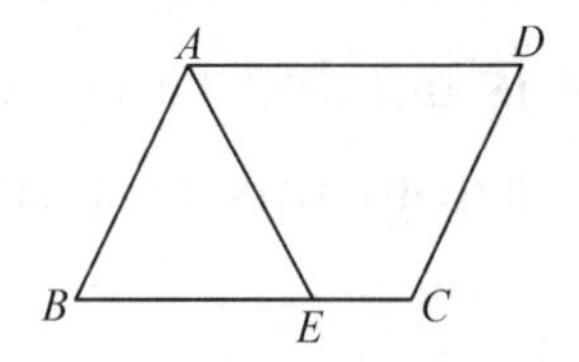

Diagram for Question 11

C. Concept problems. (20 marks in total)

(A) **Fill in the brackets.** (12 marks in total)

12 If $1.8 \times 2.5 = 4.5$, then $0.045 \div 0.18 =$ (   ).

13 5.035 035 0⋯ is a recurring decimal. Using a simple way, it is denoted as (   ).

14 If $0.8a = b \div 1.2 = c$ (a, b and c are all greater than 0), then (   ) < (   ) < (   ).

15 There are 4 classes in Grade 5. It was planned that each class would plant x trees. In fact, each class planted 5 trees more. A total of (   ) trees were planted.

16 After the expression $3x + 4y - (2x - y)$ is simplified, it is (   ).
When $x = 1.2$ and $y = 1.8$, the value of the expression is (   ).

17 The perimeter of a right-angled triangle is 60 cm. The two non-hypotenuse sides are 15 cm and 20 cm. Then the height on the hypotenuse of the right-angled triangle is (   ) cm.

18 A teacher bought 8 footballs and 15 basketballs from a sports goods store and paid 916 yuan in total. Each football is 12 yuan cheaper than each basketball. One football and one basketball cost (   ) yuan in total.

19 A clothes shop sold 50 sets of shirts in the morning and 62 sets of the same type of shirts in the afternoon. It received 720 yuan more from the sale in the afternoon than in the morning. The store received (   ) yuan from the sale in total on that day.

20 There is a mixed decimal number, whose whole number part is a and decimal part is b ($a > 0$, and $0 < b < 1$). If b is increased to 7 times its original value and then added to the original mixed decimal number, the result is 10. The least mixed decimal number required is (   ).

21 A rectangular piece of paper is 21 cm long and 12 cm wide. Some right-angled triangles each with two non-hypotenuse sides 5 cm and 4 cm are to be cut out from the paper. At most how many such triangles can be cut out?

22 If a road is repaired by Team B only, it can be completed in 60 days. Now it is repaired by Team A and Team B together and it will be completed in 24 days. Given that 1.5 kilometres of the road is repaired by Team A each day, the total length of the road is (   ) kilometres.

(B) True or false. (4 marks in total)

23 In a school, Grade 5 has 290 pupils in total in 8 classes. The statistics shows that each class has 36.25 pupils on average. (   )

24 Two triangles having equal bases and the same height can definitely form a parallelogram. (   )

25 If a dividend greater than zero is divided by a divisor not less than 1, the quotient obtained must be less than the dividend. (   )

26 In a trapezium, the top base is a dm, the bottom base is b dm, and the height is h dm. If the top base is increased by 5 dm and the others remain unchanged, then the area is increased by $2.5h$ dm^2. (　　)

(C) Multiple choice questions. (4 marks in total)

27 The expression with the same result as 3.75×1.6 is (　　).

(A) 0.375×0.16　　(B) 37.5×16

(C) 37.5×0.16　　(D) 37.5×0.016

28 Put the four numbers 3.45, $3.\dot{4}$, 3.54 and 3.448 in order from the least to the greatest. The number in the second place is (　　).

(A) 3.45　　(B) $3.\dot{4}$　　(C) 3.54　　(D) 3.448

29 The perimeter of an isosceles trapezium is 48 centimetres, the area is 96 square centimetres and the height is 8 centimetres. Then the length of the lateral sides of the isosceles trapezium is (　　).

(A) 24 centimetres　　(B) 12 centimetres

(C) 18 centimetres　　(D) 36 centimetres

30 A bag has 60 spare parts including some weighing 2 grams, some weighing 5 grams and the others weighing 9 grams. The number of spare parts weighing 2 grams is twice that weighing 5 grams. The number of spare parts weighing 5 grams is 3 times that weighing 9 grams. The weight of the bag of spare parts is (　　).

(A) 200 grams　　(B) 216 grams　　(C) 225 grams　　(D) 270 grams

Answers for reference

Chapter 1 Revising and improving

1.1 Using symbols to represent numbers

1 (1) 14.4 (2) 5.6 (3) 20 (4) 140 (5) 9 (6) 32 (7) 5 (8) 10.2 **2** (1) 6 (2) 6 (3) 3 (4) 4 (5) 6 (6) 5 **3** (1) * = 17 □ = 33 (2) ○ = 7.1 ☆ = 0.9 (3) □ = 32 ☆ = 256 (4) △ = 1.3 **4** (1) 6 (2) 4~11 (3) 12 (4) 6 (5) 7 (6) ○=7 △=6 **5** 135 9 **6** 128 252

1.2 Decimals (1)

1 (1) 1 5 7 9 2 (2) 200.304 (3) pure less (4) 10 8 0.09 **2** 0.011 6.06 120 **3** 0.560 3.000 10.200 **4** (1) 7 (2) 0.69 (3) 180 (4) 0.0036 (5) 100 (6) 10 000 (7) 0.8 (8) 280 (9) 5 500 (10) 0.47 0.0047 **5** (1) 1350 (2) 0.78 (3) 15 400 (4) 30 (5) 8 (6) 8.08 (7) 4 200 000 (8) 500 000 (9) 0.1 (10) 0.015 **6** 8 tonnes= 8000 kilograms > 7790 kilograms, Shenzhou VI Spaceship is heavier. **7** (1) 0.047 × 10 (2) 0.0034 ÷ 100 **8** (1) 3.93÷10=0.393 (g) (2) 0.2÷10×1000 = 20 (g) (3) 3.3 ÷ 100 × 10 000 = 330 (g) (4) 0.12÷100×1 000 000÷1000 = 1.2 (kg)

1.3 Decimals (2)

1 20 0.63 10 0.92 12.64 20 11 0.8 19.8 1.5 0.76 6 0.36 10 **2** (1) 101 (2) 2.07 **3** (1) 67.6 (2) 12.8 **4** (1) 14.5 (2) 10.9 (3) 54.7 (4) 61 **5** (1) B (2) A (3) B (4) A **6** (1) 10−2.8−4.2=3 (metres) (2) 580 − 42.8 = 537.2 (yuan) **7** (1) 3.4 (2) 1.7

1.4 Decimals (3)

1 (1) 8.1−5.7=2.4 7−2.4=4.6 (2) 9.8−5.74 = 4.06 4.06 + 3.28 = 7.34 **2** Tree diagram omitted, number sentence: (80−8)÷6= 12 (years old) **3** (1) 9−1.73=7.27 7.27+5.37=12.64 9−1.73+5.37=12.64 (2) 19.9−10.1=9.8 9.8−5.45=4.35 19.9−10.1−5.45=4.35 **4** (1) 4.15 (2) 39 **5** (1) 4−0.58−1.27=2.15 (metres) (2) 1.42+0.05+0.03=1.5 (metres) (3) 85.6+2.56−6.45=81.71 (tonnes) **6** 589.4+67.2−120.7+35.8=571.7 (yuan)

Unit test 1

1 0.86 1 1 7.25 52.3 9 **2** (1) 23.7 (2) 35.22 **3** (1) 185 (Checking omitted) (2) 7.19 **4** (1) 6.68 (2) 41 (3) 30 (4) 16 (5) 82.24 (6) 3 **5** (1) 14.2+8.6−0.44 = 22.36 (2) (18.9+11.2)−(2.8+3.3) = 24 **6** 3.61 − 2.12 + 3.61 = 5.1 (hundred million square kilometres) **7** 7.25−1.2+1.45 = 7.5 (tons) 38 − 7.25 − (7.25 − 1.2) − 7.5 = 17.2 (tons) **8** 2.84 − 0.55+0.17 = 2.46 (metres) **9** 880 − 80.5 − 102.9 = 696.6 (yuan) **10** 8.4−2.8−(2.8+1.9) = 0.9 (metres) **11** (1) 8.68+9.8+4.5 = 22.98 (yuan) (2) 7.55 + 2.8 + 3.6 = 13.95 (yuan) Yes, it would be enough. 15−13.95 = 1.05 (yuan) **12** 30.04 3.0404 **13** 7.80 4.10 **14** 280 0.138 1.4256 1 520 000 443 7 80 **15** (1) 16 37 (2) 13 6 **16** (1) 6 8 (2) 5.9 (3) 7 1009 (4) 19 (5) 33.3 (6) 108

Chapter 2 Multiplication and division of decimals

2.1 Multiplying decimals by whole numbers (1)

1 Xiao Dingding: 6 48 48 Xiao Pang: 58 58 464 464 46.4 Xiao Qiao: 58 464 46.4 464 10 46.4 **2** (1) 256 10 25.6 (2) 62 100 248 100 2.48 (3) 9 135 1000 1215 1000 1.215 **3** (1) Estimate: 8 × 1 = 8 Calculate: 7.2 (2) Estimate: 9 × 7 = 63 Calculate: 63.7 (3) Estimate: 11 × 3 = 33 Calculate: 32.1 (4) Estimate: 5 × 9 = 45 Calculate: 40.95 **4** (1) 3.6 × 4 = 14.4 (metres) (2) 0.75×9 = 6.75 (yuan) (3) 0.28×

8 = 2.24 (kilometres) **5** 4 + 3.8 × 9 = 38.2 (metres)

2.2 Multiplying decimals by whole numbers (2)

1 omitted **2** (1) 174 (2) 1.74 (3) 705 (4) 7.05 **3** (1) 17.25 (2) 1.725 (3) 1.725 (4) 172.5 (5) 1725 (6) 17.25 **4** (1) 1.68 (2) 50.05 (3) 261 (4) 7.65 (5) 550.8 (6) 1180 **5** (1) × 4.5 × 8 = 36 (2) × 1.36 × 250 = 340 (3) × 3.14 × 1050 = 3297 **6** (1) 39 × 0.16 = 6.24 (kilograms) (2) No, he didn't, because 4.6 × 7 = 32.2 (yuan), 32.2 yuan > 30 yuan. **7** 0.96 × (8 − 1) = 6.72 (metres)

2.3 Multiplying two decimal numbers (1)

1 475 Xiao Ya: 100 100 472.44 Xiao Qiao: one one 472.44 two **2** (1) 1000 (2) four (3) 18 1.8 1.8 0.18 (4) 1000 **3** (1) 7.83 (2) 6.205 (3) 7.884 (4) 158.4 (5) 142.83 (6) 8.484 **4** (1) 78.5 × 3.8 = 298.3 (kilometres) (2) 0.8 × 20.9 = 16.72 (tonnes) (3) 9.5 × 12.5 = 118.75 (kilometres) **5** 62.5 × 12.8 = 800 (metres) = 0.8 (kilometres)

2.4 Multiplying two decimal numbers (2)

1 0.098 two two 0.098 three **2** (1) 0.042 0.0494 0.0096 0.009 01 (2) 0.054 0.054 0.0054 0.000 54 (3) 1 (4) 8 **3** (1) 0.098 (2) 0.028 (3) 0.0384 (4) 0.0396 (5) 0.021 (6) 0.0754 **4** (1) 0.48 × 0.15 = 0.072 (square metres) (2) 0.16 × 0.35 = 0.056 (tonnes) (3) 0.3 × 0.3 × 270 = 0.09 × 270 = 24.3 (m^2), 24.3 < 24.8, therefore, they are not enough. **5** $0.\underbrace{0\cdots0}_{24\text{ zeros}}24 \times 0.\underbrace{0\cdots0}_{125\text{ zeros}}125 = 0.\underbrace{0\cdots0}_{150\text{ zeros}}3$

2.5 Multiplying two decimal numbers (3)

1 (1) 14.84 (2) 1.61 (3) 0.0336 **2** 7.2 4.8 0.72 0.072 greater than equal to less than **3** (1) > (2) < (3) < (4) > (5) < (6) > (7) = (8) = **4** (1) 0.448 (2) 10.7304 (3) 0.1494 (4) 0.048 32 (5) 0.2268 (6) 2585.6 **5** (1) C (2) A (3) D (4) C **6** (1) 3.2 × 1.4 = 4.48 (yuan) (2) 48.65 × 6 = 291.9 (kilograms) 291.9 × 0.8 = 233.52 (yuan) **7** 2.21 20.09 42.16 56.24 240.25

2.6 Multiplying three numbers, and mixed operations of multiplication with addition and subtraction

1 (1) 2.5 × (6.2 − 2.6) = 9 (2) 3.4 × (0.45 × 1.2) = 1.836 **2** (1) 7.215 (2) 9.454 (3) 0.81 (4) 2.835 (5) 17.11 (6) 441 **3** (1) (7.8 + 0.7) × 0.6 = 5.1 (2) (3.2 − 0.4) × 3.9 = 10.92 (3) 10 × 0.44 − 2.5 = 1.9 (4) (6.9 − 0.9) ÷ 2 = 3 **4** (1) 2.08 × 2.5 + 2.08 = 7.28 (metres) (2) 6.4 × 4.9 × 70 = 2195.2 (kilograms) = 2.1952 tons (3) 40 − 8 × 3.20 = 14.4 (yuan) (4) Perimeter: 0.6 × 2 × 4 = 4.8 (decimetres) Area: 0.6 × 0.6 × 4 = 1.44 (square decimetres) **5** (1) (15.2 + 2.5) × 3 − 10.6 = 42.5 (2) 30 − (1.8 × 2.6 − 1.5) = 26.82 (3) 4.5 × 5.3 − (2.5 + 1.8) = 19.55

2.7 Extending laws of multiplication with whole numbers to decimals

1 omitted **2** (1) × (2) × (3) √ (4) × **3** (1) 32 (2) 1.8 (3) 9.999 (4) 57.6 (5) 0.99 (6) 68 (7) 1100 (8) 7.8 (9) 6.5 **4** (1) (121.5 + 78.5) × 320 = 64 000 (yuan) (2) 12.5 × 16 × 2.5 = 500 (tonnes) (3) 0.25 × 0.25 × 240 = 15 (square metres) **5** 33.2667

2.8 Division of decimals by whole numbers (1)

1 (1) 1.4 84 14 14 1.4 (2) 1.34 938 7 134 1.34 **2** (1) 1.4 (2) 2.9 (3) 3.42 **3** (1) 10.8 (2) 6.4 (3) 5.6 (4) 5.46 (5) 6.4 (6) 7.64 **4** (1) 128.4 ÷ 6 = 21.4 (2) 22.8 − 22.8 ÷ 12 = 20.9 **5** (1) 7.35 ÷ 3 = 2.45 (yuan) (2) 48 × 3.6 ÷ 4 = 43.2 (kilometres) **6** (1.6 + 1.2) × 2 = 5.6 (metres), 5.6 ÷ 4 = 1.4 (metres), 1.4 × 1.4 = 1.96 (square metres)

2.9 Division of decimals by whole numbers (2)

1 2.3 2.1 6.4 6.6 1.2 1.9 5.9 1.24 **2** 0 0 dividend 9 0.01 **3** (1) 0.83 (2) 0.53 (3) 0.048 (4) 0.24 (5) 0.016 (6) 0.03 **4** (1) 12.5 ÷ 25 = 0.5 (2) (53.8 − 53.26) ÷ 54 = 0.01 **5** (1) 9.9 ÷ 18 = 0.55 (tonnes) (2) Team *B* had better work efficiency. Team *A*: 3.45 ÷ 5 = 0.69 (kilometres), Team *B*:

5.04 ÷ 7 = 0.72 (kilometres) (3) 3.25 ÷ 25 = 0.13 (tonnes) 0.13 × 40.5 = 5.265 (tonnes) (4) 2.4 ÷ 3 = 0.8 (metres) (3 + 0.8) × 2 = 7.6 (metres) ❻ Number A: 8.36 ÷ (10 + 1) = 0.76 Number B: 0.76 × 10 = 7.6

2.10 Division of decimals by whole numbers (3)

❶ 0.3 0.375 ❷ (1) 1.95 (2) 4.35 (3) 0.085 (4) 0.03 (5) 0.115 (6) 0.175 ❸ (1) 1.8 ÷ 4 = 0.45 (2) 10.8 ÷ 8 × 10 = 13.5 ❹ (1) 56.4 ÷ 24 = 2.35 (metres) (2) 2.2 ÷ 4 = 0.55 (metres) 0.55 × 0.55 = 0.3025 (square metres) (3) 28.8 ÷ 500 = 0.0576 (yuan), 38.8 ÷ 800 = 0.0485 (yuan), 0.0576 yuan > 0.0485 yuan, therefore, continental cookies are cheaper. (4) (32.6 − 1.4) ÷ 5 = 6.24 (kilograms)

❺ ① Compare by the unit price: 7.1 × 3 ÷ 4 = 5.325 (yuan), 5.325 yuan < 5.45 yuan, Aunt Zhang had a better deal. ② Compare by the total price of the four bottles: 7.1 × 3 = 21.3 (yuan), 5.45 × 4 = 21.8 (yuan), 21.3 yuan < 21.8 yuan, Aunt Zhang had a better deal.
③ Compare by the price of one litre: 5.45 ÷ 2 = 2.725 (yuan), 7.1 × 3 ÷ (2 × 4) = 2.6625 (yuan), 2.6625 yuan < 2.725 yuan, Aunt Zhang had a better deal.

2.11 Division of decimals by whole numbers (4)

❶ 0.0225 225 22.5 0.225 0.000 225 0.002 25 ❷ (1) 0.4 (2) 0.25 (3) 0.08 (4) 0.375 (5) 0.0625 (6) 4.25 ❸ (1) 65 ÷ 26 = 2.5 (2) 3 × 0.5 ÷ 12 = 0.125 ❹ (1) 1.5 ÷ 15 = 0.1 (kilometres) (2) 486 ÷ 180 = 2.7 (3) 309 ÷ 4 = 77.25 (kilometres) (4) 31 ÷ (9 − 5) = 7.75 (yuan) 7.75 × (9 + 5) = 108.5 (yuan) ❺ 30 + 2.75 + 1440 × 3 ÷ 150 = 61.55 (yuan) ❻ (8.2 − 6.2) ÷ (8 − 3) = 0.4, 6.2 − 0.4 × 3 = 5, 5 + 0.4 = 5.4

2.12 Division by a decimal number (1)

❶ 5870 90 13.78 47500 ❷ 25.6 2.56 256 0.256 25.6 0.256 ❸ 5 50 18.2 ❹ (1) C (2) D (3) B (4) A ❺ (1) 0.1 (2) 42.5 (3) 0.8 (4) 0.59 (5) 1.8 (6) 20 ❻ (1) 40 ÷ 2.5 = 16 (pieces) (2) 76.8 ÷ 1.6 + 76.8 = 124.8 (thousand sets) (3) 207.9 ÷ (2.5 + 0.2) = 77 (kilometres) ❼ Number B: 2.08 ÷ (0.3 + 1) = 1.6 Number A: 1.6 × 0.3 = 0.48

2.13 Division by a decimal number (2)

❶ 80 8 1.2 0.8 0.08 less than equal to greater than ❷ (1) < (2) > (3) > (4) > (5) < (6) = (7) = (8) < ❸ (1) 9.5 (2) 0.8 (3) 130 (4) 0.3 (5) 24 (6) 12.12 ❹ (1) 2.7 (2) 10.075 (3) 12.47 (4) 101.8 ❺ (1) C (2) A (3) A (4) C (5) D (6) B ❻ 19.2

2.14 Division by a decimal number (3)

❶ 10 7 0.02 0.7 6.7 0.5 ❷ (1) 0.35 (2) 0.36 (3) 63 (4) 1.02 (5) 3.08 (6) 375 ❸ (1) 0.3 (2) 0.27 0.011 0.0036 (3) > < = = ❹ (1) D (2) B ❺ (1) 18.6 ÷ 2.5 = 7 (pieces)……1.1 (metres) (2) 29 ÷ 1.25 = 23 (bottles)……0.25 (litres) (3) 10 ÷ 2.6 = 3 (pens)……2.2 (yuan) (4) (20 − 5) ÷ 2.5 + 2 = 8 (hours) ❻ 11.9 − 1.1 = 10.8 = 1 × 10.8 = 2 × 5.4 = 3 × 3.6 = 4 × 2.7 = 5 × 2.16 = 6 × 1.8 = 8 × 1.35 = 9 × 1.2. There are 8 different results and they are: 10.8, 5.4, 3.6, 2.7, 2.16, 1.8, 1.35, 1.2

2.15 Recurring decimals

❶ (1) $2.\dot{9}$ (2) not a recurring number (3) $4.1\dot{3}$ (4) $5.125\dot{1}\dot{2}$ (5) not a recurring number (6) $6.\dot{4}1\dot{6}$ (7) $5.0\dot{2}\dot{7}$ (8) $7.\dot{0}19\dot{2}$ (9) not a recurring number ❷ (1) $0.\dot{2}$ (2) $1.\dot{6}\dot{3}$ (3) $5.3\dot{2}\dot{7}$ ❸ < > < = < = > = ❹ (1) × (2) × (3) × (4) × (5) √ ❺ $1.1\dot{2}\dot{1} > 1.\dot{1}2\dot{1} > 1.12\dot{1} >$ 1.121 ❻ (1) C (2) C (3) D ❼ 85 × (2.60 ÷ 2) = 110.5 (yuan) ❽ $0.1234\dot{5}$ ❾ 4 449

2.16 Calculation with calculators

❶ (1) 285.7512 (2) 35.8926 (3) 1589.28 (4) 36.8 (5) 4.42 (6) 306 ❷ ① 36 ② 4356 ③ 443 556 ④ 44 435 556 ⑤ 4 444 355 556 ⑥ 444 443 555 556 ❸ (1) 0.1 (2) $0.\dot{2}$ (3) $0.\dot{3}$ (4) $0.\dot{4}$ (5) $0.\dot{5}$ (6) $0.\dot{6}$ (7) $0.\dot{7}$ (8) $0.\dot{8}$ ❹ (1) 42 371 ÷ 90 ÷ 60 = $7.846\dot{4}8\dot{1}$ (kilometres/second)

(2) ① 0.018 × 365 = 6.57 (tonnes) ② 6.57 tonnes = 6570 kilograms, 6570 ÷ 19 ≈ 345 (barrels) ③ 345 ÷ 3 = 115 (months) 115 ÷ 12 = $9.58\dot{3}$ (years) **5** (1) 111 111 111 (2) 222 222 222 (3) 333 333 333 (4) 444 444 444 (5) 555 555 555 (6) 666 666 666 (7) 777 777 777 (8) 888 888 888 (9) 999 999 999

2.17 Approximation of products and quotients

1

	Round to the nearest one	Round to the nearest tenth	Round to the nearest hundredth
3.409	3	3.4	3.41
16.032	16	16.0	16.03
5.697	6	5.7	5.70
29.993	30	30.0	29.99

2 36.2 0.279 2.48 58.6 16.230 3.43
3 (1) 6.56 × 2.4 = 15.744 ≈ 15.74 (yuan) (2) 60 ÷ 4.5 = $13.\dot{3}$, 14 bottles are needed (3) 4.5 × 6.3018 = 28.3581 ≈ 28.36 (yuan) (4) 8000 ÷ 8.4016 ≈ 952.20 (euros) (5) 10 000 ÷ 10.0356 ≈ 996.45 (pounds) **4** 1000 ÷ 7.7386 ≈ 129.22 (US dollars), 129.22 × 6.3018 ≈ 814.32 (yuan), 814.32 yuan < 1000 yuan, he lost 1000 − 814.32 = 185.68 (yuan)

2.18 Practice and exercise

1 (1) 0.7 0.84 (2) 12.5 3.28 (3) 4 4 0.125 + 2.5 **2** (1) 0.022 23 (2) 5.0 (3) 5.2 **3** (1) 13.5 − 60.8 ÷ 16 = 9.7 (2) 1.4 × (4.25 + 5.8) = 14.07 **4** (1) 32.4 (2) 6.222 (3) 15.22 (4) 100 (5) 70 (6) 67.5 (7) 195 **5** (1) 27.8 ÷ (19.3 − 16.52) = 10 (2) (3.6 + 4.4) ÷ 4 = 2 **6** (1) 38 ÷ 1.25 = 30 (bottles)…… 0.5 (litres) (2) 13.91 ÷ (9.1 ÷ 0.7) = 1.07 (hours) (3) 10.5 − 10.5 × 8 ÷ 10 = 2.1 (kilograms) (4) 73.8 ÷ 36 × 72 = 147.6 (kilograms) (5) 8.1 × 2.5 × 2 ÷ 4.5 = 9 (kilograms) **7** (1) 44 (2) $1.1\dot{1}\dot{0}$ 1.11 (3) 5.91 (4) > = < > > < > > (5) 4.895 4.904 (6) 0.33 **8** (1) C (2) B (3) A (4) D

9 (1) × (2) √ **10** A: 3.5, B: 3.05, C: 4.05

Unit test 2

1 (1) 12 (2) 1.88 (3) 3.52 (4) 4.9
2 (1) 4.19 (2) 4.736 (3) 4.41 (4) $0.3\dot{8}$
3 (1) 72 (2) 125 (3) 369.6 (4) 8.4
4 (1) (4.8 − 0.6) ÷ 4 = 1.05 (2) 1.5 × 0.24 ÷ (2.85 + 0.75) = 0.1 **5** 85 × 2.4 ÷ 80 = 2.55 (hours) **6** 300 × 25 ÷ 15 − 300 = 200 (metres)
7 9.6 ÷ 1.25 = 7 (bottles)……0.85 (litres)
8 1 kilogram **9** 3 times **10** 4.2 × 3.8 ÷ (0.2 × 0.2) = 399 (tiles) **11** (1) 1.25 (2) 1250 (3) 0.675 **12** (1) > (2) < (3) > **13** (1) $3.14\dot{6}$ (2) $5.\dot{6}0\dot{8}$ (3) $4.1\dot{0}9\dot{2}$
14 $0.\dot{1}\dot{8}$ **15** $4.6\dot{7}$(answer may vary) **16** 99
17 0.15 **18** 7.04 6.95 **19** A **20** A
21 B **22** D **23** A

Chapter 3 Statistics

3.1 Mean

1 (1) Sum of the values Number of the values (2) 112 (3) 60 (4) 95 **2** (1) 141.5 (2) 324.8 kilograms **3** (1) 566 + 308 + 1027 + 429 = 2330 (yuan) (2) 2330 ÷ 4 = 582.5 (yuan)
4 (8 + 6 + 10 + 12 + 4) ÷ 5 = 8 (pupils)
5 (1) (138 + 152 + 140 + 145 + 155 + 143) ÷ 6 = 145.5 (centimetres) (2) (33 + 41 + 38 + 44 + 43 + 35) ÷ 6 = 39 (kilograms) **6** (98 + 94 + 92 + 95 + 100 + 97) ÷ 6 = 96 (marks) **7** 90 + (8 − 2 − 6 + 2 + 5 − 1 + 4 + 1 + 2 − 2 − 9 + 1) ÷ 15 = 90.2 (marks)

3.2 Calculation of the mean (1)

1 (1) 4.9 (2) 36.8 **2** (1) A, D (2) B
3 (10 + 8 + 10 + 7 + 12) ÷ 5 = 9.4 (questions)
4 (20 + 26 + 47 + 39) ÷ 3 = 44 (tonnes)
5 (24 × 4 + 22 × 2 + 21) ÷ 7 = 23 (pages)
6 (160 + 210) ÷ (2 + 3) = 74 (kilometres)
7 (150 + 160 + 350) ÷ (3 + 5 + 7) = 44 (kilograms)
8 (1550 + 1750) ÷ 2 = 1650 (kilograms) (1550 + 1750) ÷ (7 + 8) = 220 (kilograms) **9** (20 × 88.8 + 16 × 91.5) ÷ (20 + 16) = 90 (marks)
10 (7 × 62 − 2 × 56) ÷ (7 − 2) = 64.4

3.3 Calculation of the mean (2)

1 (1) B (2) C 2 $(150+200+180+220+160)\div 7=130$ (millilitres) 3 $(732+698+628+1254)\div 5=662.4$ (toys) 4 $(2+3+2+2+1)\div 6\approx 1.7$ (times) 5 $(65\times 2+75\times 3)\div(2+3)=71$ (kilometres) 6 $(35\times 4+48\times 2+50\times 3+34)\div 10=42$ (skips) 7 (1) $(16\times 41.5+14\times 38.5)\div(16+14)=40.1$ (kilograms) (2) $(15\times 41.8+15\times 37.2)\div(15+15)=39.5$ (kilograms) or $(41.8+37.2)\div 2=39.5$ (kilograms) (3) $(16\times 41.5+15\times 41.8)\div(16+15)\approx 41.6$ (kilograms) (4) $(14\times 38.5+15\times 37.2)\div(14+15)\approx 37.8$ (kilograms) 8 $(36\times 2+30\times 2+39\times 2)\div 2\div 3=35$

3.4 Application of the mean (1)

1 (1) 36 38 Xiao Pang (2) second

2 (1) $(56+44+60+58+47)\div 5=53$ (skips) (2) $(50+47+59+62)\div 4=54.5$ (skips) (3) Group 2 did more by 1.5 skips. 3 $238\div 3.5=68$ (kilometres/hour), $260\div 4=65$ (kilometres/hour). Car *A* travelled at a faster speed.

4 $6\div 5=1.2$ (litres), $5\div 4=1.25$ (litres), $4\div 3\approx 1.3$ (litres). Xiao Qiao's family drinks the most water per person per day. 5 $162\div 12=13.5$ (spare parts), $195\div 15=13$ (spare parts), $224\div 16=14$ (spare parts). Team 3 is the fastest. 6 (1) $36\times 48\div 32=54$ (metres/minute) (2) $36\times 48\times 2\div(48+32)=43.2$ (metres/minute)

7 $(12.8\times 2+8.8\times 3+9.8\times 5)\div(2+3+5)=10.1$ (yuan)

3.5 Application of the mean (2)

1 (1) 0.6 (2) 28 (3) 60.6 (4) 10

2 (1) $(59+63+65+60+61+64)\div 6=62$ (steps) (2) $45\times 62\div 100=27.9$ (metres) (3) $27.9\times 20=558$ (metres) (4) $446.4\div 27.9=16$ (minutes) 3 (1) $(1800+2000+2100+2400+1600+1500+2600)\div 7=2000$ (words) (2) $48\,000\div 2000=24$ (days) (3) $2000\times 365\div 10\,000=730$ (thousand words) 4 $(64\times 7-70\times 4)\div 3=56$ (kilometres/hour) 5 $(84\times 2+92\times 2-85)\div 3=89$ 6 $(98-91.2)\div(91.4-91.2)=34$ (pupils)

3.6 Application of the mean (3)

1 (1) 51 (2) 51 (3) 51 (4) 54

2 (1) $(240+300+360+380+420)\div 5=340$ (grams) (2) $340\times 5-330\times 4=380$ (grams)

3 (1) $(92\times 3+95\times 2)\div(3+2)=93.2$ (marks) (2) Xiao Ya: $95-4\div 2=93$ (marks), Xiao Pang: $93-2=91$ (marks), Xiao Qiao: $91-1=90$ (marks), Xiao Dingding: $92\times 3-91-90=95$ (marks). 4 $148\times 4-135-146-150=161$ (skips) 5 $(92.5\times 38+95+100)\div 40=92.75$ (marks) 6 $3600\times 2\div(4.5+5.1)=750$ (kilometres/hour) 7 $(89.5-80.5)\div(88.7-88.4)=30$ (pupils) 8 $(128+156+164+14)\div 3\times 4=616$ (spare parts)

Unit test 3

1 95 2 143 161 3 27 4 15 5 46 6 5.5 7 48 8 48.8 9 29.6 10 93 11 80 12 126 18 13 19.8 14 97 15 19 16 B 17 D 18 D 19 B 20 C 21 $(147+153\times 2)\div 3=151$ (workers) 22 Classroom A: $120\div 50=2.4$ (pupils), Classroom B: $150\div 60=2.5$ (pupils). Classroom B is more crowded.

23 (1) $(30+28+15+23+40+32)\div 7=24$ (minutes) (2) $24\times 30=720$ (minutes)

24 (1) $(300\times 2+350\times 3+330)\div 6=330$ (kilograms) (2) $330\times 12=3960$ (kilograms)

25 (1) $(4.2+4.8+4.6+4.8)\div 4\div 10=0.46$ (metres) (2) $(120+136+128+130+126)\div 5\times 0.46=58.88$ (metres) (3) $0.46\times 8500\div 1000=3.91$ (kilometres) 26 $(36\times 12+630)\div(12+18)=35.4$ (metres) 27 $2400-200=2200$ (dolls), $2200+600=2800$ (dolls), $(2400+2200+2400+2800)\div 4=2450$ (dolls)

28 (1) Class (1): $32\times 90=2880$ (marks), Class (2): $28\times 91.5=2562$ (marks), Class (3): $30\times 88=2640$ (marks) (2) $(2880+2562+2640)\div 3=2694$ (marks) (3) $(2880+2562+2640)\div(32+28+30)=89.8$ (marks)

29 (1) Class 5 (1): $(12+8+10+9+11+9+8+6+15+16)\div 10=10.4$ (goals), Class 5 (2): $(8+9+12+11+5+10+12+9+14)\div 9=10$ (goals) (2) $(104+90)\div(10+9)\approx 10.2$ (goals)

30 $(128-120)\times 15\div(120-115)=24$ (workers)

Chapter 4 Simple equations

4.1 Using letters to represent numbers (1)

1 (1) 12 (2) 2 (3) 5 (4) 5 (5) 64 (6) 4 25 **2** (1) $8m$ (2) $3xy$ (3) $6(9+a)$ (4) $n+0.5a$ (5) a^2 (6) $3b$ **3** (1) Associative law of addition (2) Distributive law of multiplication (3) Quotient property of equality (4) Property of subtraction **4** (1) $180°-a°-b°$ (2) $180°-2a°$ (3) $C\div 4$ (4) $C\div A$ (5) $S\div a$ (6) 3 6 12 x $2x$ $4x$ **5** $65t$ $210\div v$ $s\div 6$ $480\div x$ $x\div 25$ $30x$ $8.5b$ $x\div y$ $z\div a$ **6** $a\div 3$ $a\div 3-2$ $a\div 3+2$ **7** $A=7$ $B=6$ $C=1$ $D=8$

4.2 Using letters to represent numbers (2)

1 (1) C (2) D (3) B (4) C **2** (1) $100-(a+b)$ (2) $5\div x+n$ (3) $6s-2$ (4) $320-12m$ (5) $5(80+b)$ (6) $6(b+90)$ **3** (1) $50+n$ (2) $m+2n$ (3) $50+m+n$ (4) $2m+3n$ (5) $m-n$ **4** (1) $85t$ (2) $m\div 6$ (3) $24-n$ (4) $3(a+b)$ **5** (1) The total value of the sales for the whole day: $175a$ yuan. The sales value in the morning was $25a$ yuan less than that in the afternoon (2) $[x\div(m+2.5)]$ days **6** In the table, from left to right: 1 4 9 16 25 36 … n^2 $2008^2=4\,032\,064$

4.3 Simplification and evaluation (1)

1 (1) $9x$ (2) $9(b-a)$ (3) $13x+7$ (4) 0 (5) $12s+20t$ (6) $24x+75y$ (7) $60a$ (8) $4k$ (9) $9x$ (10) $20y$ (11) $59x$ (12) $18n$ **2** (1) × (2) × (3) × **3** (1) $3a$ (2) $2x+3$ (3) $10y+5x$ (4) $11x$ (5) $12a$ $6b$ **4** (1) $50\div 10\times 3a=15a$ (kilograms) (2) $[(21+n)\div 2]$ flowers $[(21+n)\div(m+2)]$ flowers (3) $x+6x+6=7x+6$ **5** The area: $15a$ square centimetres The perimeter: $2(15+a)$ centimetres or: $2(3a+5)$ centimetres **6** $2a+2b+4(a-b)=(6a-2b)$ centimetres

4.4 Simplification and evaluation (2)

1 7 21 35 49 63 **2** (1) $(6c+s)$ metres (2) 500 metres **3** $4a$ a^2 20 25 **4** (1) $10x$, 25 (2) $10y$, 20 (3) $20m-30n$, 26 (4) $28a+5b$, 17 **5** (1) ① $26x$ ② 520 (2) ① $(4a+b)$ kilometres ② 520 kilometres (3) ① $(3a-4)$ pupils ② 68 pupils **6** $(2m-n)$ yuan, 15 yuan

4.5 Equations (1)

1 (1) × (2) × (3) √ (4) × (5) √ **2** (1) C (2) D (3) C (4) B **3** $x+8=y$ $4y=30$ **4** (1) $2x=36$ (2) $45-x=15$ (3) $3x+12=72$ (4) $2(x+3)=48$ (5) $y\div 2=25$ (6) $10\div 20+x=8$ (7) $2x-5\times 3=1$ (8) $4y-15\times 9=5$ **5** $2a=3b$, $2(3a+b)$cm or: $2(a+4b)$cm, $2a(a+b)$cm^2 or: $3b(a+b)$cm^2 $b=4$ cm, 44 cm, 120 cm^2

4.6 Equations (2)

1 (1) a solution to the equation (2) The process to find the solution (3) $y=15$ (4) $x=1.4$ **2** (1) D (2) C **3** (1) $x=3.14$ (2) $x=35.8$ (3) $x=4.8$ (4) $x=1.6$ (5) $x=0$ (6) $x=6.76$ **4** (1) $40-x=28$, $x=12$ (2) $y+5=152$, $y=147$ (3) $7s=2.8\times 1000$, $s=400$ (4) $a\div 25=3$, $a=75$ **5** $x=3.2$, $y=4.8$

4.7 Equations (3)

1 (1) $x=3.5$ (2) $x=16.8$ (3) $x=18$ (4) $x=10$ (5) $x=5$ (6) $x=2$ (7) $x=2.3$ (8) $x=7$ (9) $x=3.5$ (10) $x=9.9$ **2** (1) $4x+3.2=9.8$, $x=1.65$ (2) $5(12-x)=40$, $x=4$ (3) $3x-102=78$, $x=60$ (4) $5.4\div(x+1.8)=2$, $x=0.9$ **3** $4x=x+4.5$, $x=1.5$ $3y=4x$ or: $3y=x+4.5$, $y=2$

4.8 Equations (4)

1 (1) $x=2.25$ (2) $x=3$ (3) $x=1.5$ (4) $x=2.9$ (5) $x=0.8$ (6) $x=2.5$ (7) $x=4.5$ (8) $x=0.6$ (9) $x=3.1$ (10) $x=1.5$ **2** (1) $4(3.6+x)=26.8$, $x=3.1$ (2) $1.6x+2.4x=10$, $x=2.5$ (3) $7x=4x+2.7$, $x=0.9$ (4) $8(7.2-x)=4x$, $x=4.8$ **3** $5x+2.4=9x-5.6$, $x=2$ **4** $x+2x+3x=60$, $x=10$

4.9 Writing equations to solve problems (1)

1 (1) $x=55$ (2) $x=0.5$ (3) $x=3.7$ (4) $x=7.5$ **2** (1) $105-x=34$, $x=71$ (2) $98-x=55$, $x=43$ (3) $480\div x=32$, $x=15$ (4) $64\div x=2$, $x=32$ (5) $1.5x-0.3=1.8$, $x=1.4$ (6) $x\div 4+3=11.5$, $x=34$ (7) $x+6\times 65=470$, $x=80$ (8) $6+4x=20$, $x=3.5$ **3** $x-3.5=4.5\times 1.2$, $x=8.9$ **4** $2(11+x)=36$, $x=7$

4.10 Writing equations to solve problems (2)

❶ (1) $x=1.8$ (2) $x=7.5$ (3) $x=0.9$ (4) $x=1.6$ ❷ (1) $4x+12=80$, $x=17$ (2) $1.5x-3=18$, $x=14$ (3) $3x+1.5=15$, $x=4.5$ (4) $2x-4700=6300$, $x=5500$ (5) $2x+14=78$, $x=32$ (6) $3x=28+8$, $x=12$ (7) $4x-19=2565$, $x=646$ (8) $x\div2+25=375$, $x=700$ ❸ $2(x-16)=50+12$, $x=47$

4.11 Writing equations to solve problems (3)

❶ (1) $x=11$ (2) $x=2$ (3) $x=15$ (4) $x=10$ ❷ (1) $3x-30=150$, $x=60$ (2) $2x+8=56$, $x=24$ (3) $3x+2=35$, $x=11$ (4) $3x=36+24$, $x=20$ (5) $5x-250=2500$, $x=550$ (6) $(x-4)\div3=12$, $x=40$ (7) $20\times2.4+16x=72$, $x=1.5$ (8) $9(x-15)=108$, $x=27$ ❸ $6(x-3)=33-3$, $x=8$

Unit test 4

❶ (1) $x=5$ (2) $x=2.6$ (3) $x=34.4$ (4) $x=4.6$ (5) $x=10$ (6) $x=5.6$ (7) $x=3.45$ (8) $x=15$ ❷ (1) 6 (2) 24.5 ❸ (1) $2.5x+5=25$, $x=8$ (2) $6.5x-4x=12$, $x=4.8$ (3) $8(x-5)\div3=120$, $x=50$ ❹ $35-8x=1.4$, $x=4.2$ ❺ $3x-14=55$, $x=23$ ❻ $0.4\times8-x\div2=0.5$, $x=5.4$ ❼ $20x=5800+440$, $x=312$ ❽ $2(x-40)=800$, $x=440$ ❾ $2(x-8)=40+4$, $x=30$ ❿ $2.4\div x$ ⓫ $a+3$ ⓬ $a-3$ ⓭ $2x+10$ ⓮ $3a$ $8a$ ⓯ $2x-24$ 1280 ⓰ $0.25a^2$ ⓱ Xiao Gang ⓲ × ⓳ √ ⓴ × ㉑ √ ㉒ √ ㉓ C ㉔ B ㉕ C ㉖ B ㉗ C

Chapter 5 Let's practise geometry

5.1 Parallelograms (1)

❶ *AB* *CD* *AD* *BC* parallel parallelogram diagonals ❷ equal equal ❸ rectangle ❹ square ❺ rectangles squares ❻ ①④ ❼ are not ❽ (1) √ (2) × (3) × (4) √ (5) × ❾ omitted ❿ (1) A (2) B, C, D ⓫ 18 ⓬ 7 centimetres 1 centimetre plus 6 centimetres 5 centimetres 2 centimetres plus 3 centimetres

5.2 Parallelograms (2)

❶ height base ❷ height ❸ *AF* *BC* *AD* ❹ equal ❺ *AC* *DE* ❻ 2 ❼ rectangle parallelogram ❽ (1) B (2) C (3) D ❾ omitted ❿ omitted ⓫ A ⓬ 10 ⓭ 20

5.3 Area of a parallelogram

❶ 4.8 m^2 16.8 dm^2 0.5 dm 3.2 cm ❷ (1) 180 cm^2 (2) 240 cm^2 (3) 75 cm^2 ❸ (1) B (2) C ❹ (1) $10.8\div2.4=4.5$ (m) (2) $4.5\times(4.5-1.3)=14.4$ (dm^2) (3) $28\times15\times45=18\,900$ (yuan) (4) $(36\div2-7.8)\times5=51$ (cm^2) ❺ B ❻ *ABFE*, *BCFE*, *CDFE*, *BFGE*

5.4 Area of a triangle (1)

❶ 0.9 m^2 1.08 dm^2 0.033 m^2 2.25 cm^2 ❷ omitted ❸ *BE* *BC* *AB* *CF* ❹ (1) $8\times5\div2=20$ (cm^2) (2) $15\times12\div2=90$ (cm^2) (3) $4\times3\div2=6$ (cm^2) ❺ (1) × (2) × (3) √ (4) √ ❻ (1) $18\times(18\div2)\div2=81$ (dm^2) (2) $24\times(24\times3+3)\div2=900$ (cm^2) (3) $32\times(32-7)\div2=400$ (cm^2) $=4$ (dm^2) ❼ $6\times6\div2=18$ (cm^2) ❽ $3.6\times4.8\div2=8.64$ (cm^2)

5.5 Area of a triangle (2)

❶ (1) $7\times6\div2=21$ (cm^2) (2) $12\times5\div2=30$ (cm^2) (3) $12\times9\div2=54$ (cm^2) ❷ (1) $20\times2\div8=5$ (cm) (2) $32.4\times2\div3.6=18$ (m) (3) $15.36\times2\div6.4=4.8$ (dm) ❸ (1) $18\times(18+8)\div2=234$ (m^2) (2) $(24+6)\times(16+3)\div2-24\times16\div2=93$ (m^2) (3) $(66\div6-4)\times6\div2=21$($dm^2$) (4) $(24\times2\div6)\times(6+5)\div2=44$ (cm^2) ❹ (1) 5 (2) 6 (3) 20 (4) 2.4 ❺ $30\times12\div2=180$ (cm^2)

5.6 Trapezia

❶ (1) trapezium (2) right-angled trapezium isosceles trapezium (3) height (4) triangle ❷ 2 ❸ 4 7 5 2 5 6 5 9 3 ❹ (1) × (2) √ (3) √ (4) √ ❺ omitted ❻ (1) B (2) D (3) C ❼ 30 ❽ (1) √ (2) √ (3) √ (4) × (5) √ (6) ×

5.7 Area of a trapezium (1)

❶ (1) $(5.5+3.5)\times4\div2=18$ (cm^2) (2) $(5+8)\times3.4\div2=22.1$ (cm^2) (3) $(9+15)\times8\div$

$2=96$ (cm²) **2** (1) 50 (2) 54 (3) 36 (4) triangle 18 (5) 102 **3** (1) D (2) D **4** (1) $(20+28)\times15\div2=360$ (m²) (2) $17\times2-1=33$ (m), $33\div3=11$ (m), $(17+33)\times11\div2=275$ (m²) (3) $(10+20)\times11\div2\times500=82\,500$ (yuan) **5** $(30-5\times2)\times4\div2=40$ (cm²)

5.8 Area of a trapezium (2)

1 7.8 3 19.5 2.7 **2** (1) $42\times2\div(8.8+5.2)=6$ (cm) (2) $120\times2\div8-18.5=11.5$ (m) **3** (1) $1.52\times2\div0.8-1.4=2.4$ (m) (2) $20.16\times2\div(5.6+5.6+1.4)=3.2$ (cm) (3) $(3+4+3)\times3\div2=15$ (cm²) $(4+3)\times4\div2=14$ (cm²) (4) $(128\times2\div8-4)\div2=14$ (cm) (5) $60\times2\div12=10$ (cm), $(12+16)\times10\div2=140$ (cm²) **4** $28\times2\div(5+2)=8$ (cm) $(8-5+8-2)\times8\div2=36$ (cm²)

5.9 Areas of composite figures

1 $(5+8)\times(6-4)\div2+8\times4=45$ (cm²) $(4+6)\times(8-5)\div2+5\times6=45$ (cm²) $6\times8-(8-5)\times(6-4)\div2=45$ (cm²) $(5+8)\times6\div2+4\times(8-5)\div2=45$ (cm²) $(6+4)\times8\div2+5\times(6-4)\div2=45$ (cm²) **2** 132 cm² **3** (1) 67 cm² (2) 39 cm² (3) 58 cm² **4** (1) $4\times3\div2+4\times(12-4)\div2=22$ (dm²) (2) $(14+6)\div2=10$ (dm), $(10+6)\times(10-6)\div2=32$ (dm²)

5.10 Practice and exercise

1 (1) D (2) C **2** $(40-2)\times(30-2)=1064$ (m²) **3** $(20-6)\times6\div2=42$ (m²) **4** (1) 79.5 cm² (2) 35.95 cm² **5** 101.25 cm² **6** $12\times12\div2-24=48$ (cm²), $48\times2\div12=8$ (cm), $24\times2\div8=6$ (cm), $6\times12\div2=36$ (cm²)

Unit test 5

1 omitted **2** (1) 63 m² (2) 17 cm² (3) 7.2 dm² **3** (1) 8 m (2) 6 dm **4** $(66\div2-18)\times12=180$ (cm²) **5** (1) $64\times2\div(6+10)=8$ (cm) (2) $10\times8\div2-15=25$ (cm²) **6** (1) $12\times2\div4=6$ (cm), $(15-6)\times4\div2=18$ (cm²) (2) 63 (cm²) **7** $(12+18)\times16\div2\div100\times50=120$ (yuan) **8** $120\times(120\div3)\div2\times75.8\div1000=181.92$ (kilograms) **9** $36\times25\div1.5\times2\div32=37.5$ (cm) **10** $(100\times90)\div(6\times5\div2)=600$ (triangles) **11** $2.88\div(1.6\times1.5\div2\times2)=1.2$ (kilograms) **12** $108\times2\div(10+10-2)\times10=120$ (m²) **13** √ **14** √ **15** × **16** C **17** B **18** C **19** 67.5 **20** 38 **21** 4.8 **22** 4 **23** 3.6 **24** 7.1 **25** 45 **26** 66

Chapter 6 Consolidation and enhancement

6.1 Mixed four operations with decimals (1)

1 (1) 9.9 (2) 4.2 (3) 2.1 (4) 1.6 (5) 9.7 (6) 2.1 **2** (1) 25.2 (2) 14.27 (3) 2.1 (4) $1.6\dot{2}\dot{4}$ **3** (1) 4.67 (2) 10 (3) 1200 (4) 48 **4** (1) 1801.2 23.7 (2) 0.24 8 5.6 4 (3) *C A* (4) 3.6 **5** (1) √ (2) × **6** (1) A (2) C **7** $18\div(0.6\times60)=0.5$ (kilometres/minute) $(0.6\times60)\div18=2$ (minutes) **8** 120 numbers 37 35 412

6.2 Mixed four operations with decimals (2)

1 (1) 1.9 (2) 11.76 (3) 6.4 (4) 3.6 **2** (1) 18.96 (2) 1.12 (3) 33.8 (4) 0.22 (5) 19.13 (6) 22.5 (7) 59.755 (8) 10 **3** (1) 21.7 (2) 20 (3) 10 (4) 100 (5) 1.92 (6) 6 (7) 450 (8) 53 **4** $25\times12\times140=42\,000$ (spare parts) $42\,000\div(12-2)\div(140+10)-25=3$ (workers) **5** $2\times3\div(13-4\times3)=6$, $6\times4+2=26$

6.3 Application of decimals — water, electricity and gas bills

1 $158\times0.617+96\times0.307=126.958\approx127.0$ yuan **2** (1) $83.13\div1.63=51$ (cubic metres) (2) $51\times0.9\times1.3=59.67$ (yuan) (3) $83.13+59.67=142.8$ (yuan) **3** $412-348=64$ (cubic metres) $64\times2.5=160$ (yuan) **4** $1000\times0.9+(1120-1000)\times1.5=1080$ (yuan) **5** (1) $5+1.2\times6=12.2$ (yuan) (2) $(23-5)\div1.2=15$ (kilometres) **6** $(5\times3+25\times0.9)\div30=1.25$ (yuan)

6.4 Writing equations to solve problems (4)

1 (1) $x=4.5$ (2) $x=0.4$ (3) $x=6.1$ (4) $x=3.5$ **2** $50-4x=6$, $x=11$ **3** $80x-200=40$, $x=3$ **4** $3.5x+2.5=20$, $x=5$ **5** $16.8\div2\times5+x=50$, $x=8$ **6** $2(9.5+x)=32$, $x=6.5$ **7** $x+2\times6.8=30$, $x=$

16.4 **8** $16 \times 27.5 + 12x = 800$, $x = 30$ **9** $3x + 4 \times 8 = 68$, $x = 12$ **10** $6(x - 40) = 90$, $x = 55$ **11** $5(x + 10) + 8x = 375$, $x = 25$

6.5 Writing equations to solve problems (5)

1 (1) $x = 1.25$ (2) $x = 5$ (3) $x = 22$ (4) $x = 2$ **2** $6x + 40 = 1240$, $x = 200$ **3** $3x - 32 = 370$, $x = 134$ **4** $4x + 5 \times 34 = 350$, $x = 45$ **5** $4.5x + 12 = 30$, $x = 4$ **6** $4(x + 4) = 58$, $x = 10.5$ **7** $248 - 18x = 112 - 26$, $x = 9$ **8** $3 \times 24 + x \div 2 = 95$, $x = 46$ **9** $4x + 7 \times 1.6 + 0.6 = 15$, $x = 0.8$ **10** $3 + 2 \times 4 + 5x = 18$, $x = 1.4$ **11** $72(x + 2x + 5) = 7920$, $x = 35$

6.6 Areas of figures (1)

1 omitted **2** $(15 + 21) \times 34 \div 2 = 612$ (cm^2) $14 \times 6 = 84$ (cm^2) **3** $29.64 \times 2 \div (4.6 + 4.6 + 2.2) = 5.2$ (cm) **4** $6 \times 6 + 4 \times 4 - 6 \times 6 \div 2 - 4 \times (6 + 4) \div 2 = 14$ (cm^2) **5** (1) $CF = 5 \times 2 = 10$ (cm), $S_{\triangle BCD} = (5 + 10) \times 8 \div 2 = 60$ (cm^2), $S_{\text{trapezium}CDEF} = (5 + 10) \times 8 \div 2 = 60$ (cm^2), so they are of the equal area. (2) $AE = 8 \div 2 = 4$ (cm), $[(5 + 10) \times (4 + 8) \div 2] \div (4 \times 5 \div 2) = 9$ **6** (1) $(9 - 6 + 9) \times 9 \div 2 = 54$ (cm^2) (2) $6 \times 6 - 9 \times 6 \div 2 = 9$ (cm^2) **7** $54 \div 2 \div 3 \times 2 \div 3 = 6$ (cm^2)

6.7 Areas of figures (2)

1 $6 \times 8 + (8 - 4) \times (10 - 6) \div 2 = 56$ (cm^2) **2** $DE = 20 - 5 = 15$ (cm), $BF = 20 - 4 = 16$ (cm), $20 \times 20 - 20 \times 15 \div 2 - 20 \times 16 \div 2 - 5 \times 4 \div 2 = 80$ (cm^2) **3** (1) $6 \times 6 \div 2 = 18$ (cm^2) (2) $(10 + 10 - 6) \times 6 \div 2 = 42$ (cm^2) (3) $10 \times 10 \div 2 \div 2 = 25$ (cm^2) (4) $42 - 25 = 17$ (cm^2) **4** $24 \div 4 = 6$ (cm), $6 - 2 = 4$ (cm), $6 \times 6 - 6 \times 4 \div 2 - 6 \times 2 \div 2 - 2 \times 4 = 10$ (cm^2) **5** (1) $90 \div (1 + 1.5) = 36$ (cm^2) (2) $BC = 36 \times 2 \div 8 = 9$ (cm), $CD = 90 \times 2 \div 9 - 8 = 12$ (cm) **6** $9 \div 3 = 3$ (cm^2), $9 \times 3 = 27$ (cm^2), $3 + 9 + 9 + 27 = 48$ (cm^2)

6.8 Mathematics plaza — calculation of time

1 (1) 22 minutes 30 seconds (2) 9 hours (3) 4 minutes 51 seconds **2** 11:33 **3** 8:50 **4** $35 \times 4 + 20 + 50 = 210$ minutes = 3 hours 30 minutes, 8:05 + 3 hours 30 minutes = 11:35 **5** 3 hours 39 minutes **6** 6 minutes 28 seconds **7** 20:20 − 18:30 = 1 hour 50 minutes = 110 minutes, $110 \times 7 = 770$ (minutes) = 12 hours 50 minutes **8** leave home at 18:45, get back home at 22:10. **9** (1) 21:50. (2) $600 - 100 = 500$ (people), $(50 \times 4 + 80 \times 3) \times 500 \times 7 = 1\,540\,000$ (yuan) or 1.54 million (yuan).

6.9 Mathematics plaza — coding

1 (1) six (2) eight (3) eighteen **2** code of the provincial-level government of residence code of the prefecture or prefecture-level city government of residence code of district or county government of residence year, month and date of birth code of the local police station gender verification code **3** Xiao Ming — 31010719950207×× 54 Xiao Ming's father — 31010719650324×× 34 Xiao Ming's aunt in Beijing — 11010519690820×× 62 Xiao Ming's grandpa — 31010719390519×× 57 Xiao Ming's grandma — 31010719421208×× 68 **4** Xiao Zhang: 17 November 1984 male Xiao Wang: 1 December 2004 female Xiao Liu: 17 May 1969 male Xiaojun: 5 August 1992 female **5** Shanghai: 021 Beijing: 010 Nanjing: 025 Chongqing: 023 Tianjin: 022 Shenzhen: 0755 **6** C **7** omitted **8** omitted

Unit test 6

1 (1) 32 (2) 87 (3) 6.96 (4) 0.08 **2** (1) 41.99 (2) $0.2\dot{0}\dot{9}$ **3** (1) $x = 12.5$ (2) $x = 1.5$ **4** (1) 5.4 (2) 0 (3) 0.5 (4) 36 (5) 0.5 (6) 7.28 **5** $30 \times 40 \div (30 - 5) = 48$ (days) **6** $4x + 2 \times 7 = 30$, $x = 4$ **7** $7x = 90 + 2 \times 480$, $x = 150$ **8** $8x + 2 = 800 \div 16$, $x = 6$ **9** (1) $10 + (8 - 3) \times 2 = 20$ (yuan) (2) $(30 - 10 - 2 \times 7) \div 3 + 10 = 12$ (kilometres) **10** $3.5 \times 10 + (10 + 7) \times 8 \div 2 = 103$ (m^2) **11** (1) a^2 $1.5a$ (2) 120 48 **12** B **13** B **14** D **15** B **16** √ **17** √ **18** √ **19** × **20** 0.00648 0.0018 **21** 46 **22** 72 36 81 **23** $2m + 4$ 15 **24** 2.1 **25** 6

Mid-term test

1 (1) 30 (2) 0.48 (3) 1.2 (4) 7.48

(5) 0.04 (6) 0.07 **2** (1) 10.25 (2) 0.1 (3) 11.16 (4) 7.2 **3** (1) 0.9 (2) 7.8 (3) 54 (4) 2.08 **4** (1) 1.2×1.2+2.2÷2 = 2.54 (2) (2.7+1.9)÷(10.8−1.6) = 0.5 **5** 100÷0.55 = 181 (bottles)……0.45 (litres) **6** 0.061×25+0.025 = 1.55 (kilograms) **7** 1.8×1000÷3×8 = 4800 (sleepers) **8** 1.2×(45−3)÷45 = 1.12 (kilometres) **9** (18×36+12×34)÷(18+12) = 35.2 (kilograms) **10** 20×2+4.5×3 = 53.5 (yuan) **11** Plan One: 30×7+40×4 = 370 (yuan) Plan Two: 30×4+40×8 = 440 (yuan) Plan Three: 30×1+40×12 = 510 (yuan) **12** 4.036 56 **13** > < **14** 9.95 10.0 **15** 34 **16** 17.1 **17** 12 **18** 4 **19** 60.04 **20** 5.6 **21** × **22** × **23** × **24** √ **25** √ **26** B **27** C **28** D **29** D **30** A

End of term test

1 (1) 0.18 (2) 9 (3) 16 (4) 1.04 (5) 0.20 (6) $3.1\dot{6}$ **2** (1) $x = 0.4$ (2) $x = 2.5$ (3) $x = 1$ (4) $x = 1.6$ **3** (1) 70 (2) 196.48 (3) 129 (4) 870 (5) 1.5 (6) 5.94 **4** (1) $4x - 5.1 = 3.5 \times 0.6$, $x = 1.8$ (2) 14.85÷[(8.7+1.3)×2.5] = 0.594 **5** (76+78+80+78)÷4 = 78 (steps), 50÷78 ≈ 0.64 (metres) **6** 120×30÷(30−5)−120 = 24 (pieces) **7** Let the number of pear trees be x, the number of peach trees is $(2x-10)$. $x+2x-10=200$, $x=70$, $2x-10=130$ **8** (16+22)×3÷2×0.5×2 = 57 (kilograms) **9** (7539−7389)×0.617+(2690−2552)×0.307 = 134.916 (yuan) ≈ 134.92 (yuan) **10** 32÷4 = 8 (cm), 8×8−8×(8÷2)÷2 = 48 (cm^2) **11** 24÷4×(11+4) = 90 (cm^2) **12** 0.25 **13** $5.0\dot{3}\dot{5}$ **14** c b a **15** $4x+20$ **16** $x+5y$ 10.2 **17** 12 **18** 76 **19** 6720 **20** 3.875 **21** 24 **22** 60 **23** √ **24** × **25** × **26** √ **27** C **28** D **29** B **30** B

Notes

Notes

Notes

Notes